Connectivity
FOUNDATIONS

CONNECTING PEOPLE THROUGH ENGLISH

WORKBOOK

Joan Saslow

Allen Ascher

**Connectivity Foundations
Workbook**

Copyright © 2022 by Pearson Education, Inc.

All rights reserved.

No part of this publication may be reproduced, stored in a retrieval system, or transmitted in any form or by any means, electronic, mechanical, photocopying, recording, or otherwise, without the prior permission of the publisher.

Pearson Education, 221 River Street, Hoboken, NJ 07030 USA

Text composition: ElectraGraphics, Inc.

Photo Credits:

Welcome Unit

Page (1,1): Ian Allenden/123RF; 1 (1,2): Dean Drobot/Shutterstock; 1 (1,3): Fizkes/Shutterstock; 1 (1,4): Jacob Lund/Shutterstock; 1 (1,5): Michaeljung/Shutterstock; 1 (left): ProStockStudio/Shutterstock; 1 (right): Yulia M/Shutterstock; 1 (bottom): Fizkes/123RF; 2 (top left): ArtAdisorn/Shutterstock; 2 (top center): ArtAdisorn/Shutterstock; 2 (top right): ArtAdisorn/Shutterstock; 2 (bottom): Stephen Coburn/Shutterstock.

Unit 1

Page 3 (1,1): Paffy/Shutterstock; (1,2): Sergey Novikov/123RF; 3 (1,3): Layland Masuda/Shutterstock; 3 (1,4): Michaeljung/Shutterstock; 3 (1,5): Valentyna Smordova/123RF; 3 (1,6): WAYHOME studio/Shutterstock; 3 (1,6 inset): Rob Marmion/Shutterstock; 3 (3a): Wavebreakmedia/Shutterstock; 3 (3b): Wavebreakmedia/Shutterstock; 3 (3c): Stockyimages/123RF; 3 (3d): Michaeljung/Shutterstock; 3 (3e): Shutterstock; 3 (3f): ADS Portrait/Shutterstock; 4 (1,1): ESB Professional/Shutterstock; 4 (1,2): Angelo Giampiccolo/Shutterstock; 4 (1,3): Dima Fadeev/Shutterstock; 4 (1,4): Dmitry Kalinovsky/Shutterstock; 4 (1,5): Aabeele/Shutterstock; 4 (2,1): ImageFlow/Shutterstock; 4 (2,2): Shestakoff/Shutterstock; 4 (2,3): Sirtravelalot/Shutterstock; 4 (2,4): Mtr/Shutterstock; 4 (2,5): Stanislav Komogorov/123RF; 5: StockLite/Shutterstock; 9: DFree/Shutterstock; 10 (1a): Alexander Morozov/123RF; 10 (1b): Ermolaev Alexander/Shutterstock; 10 (1c): MedusArt/Shutterstock; 10 (1d): Andrii Torianyk/123RF; 10 (1e): Oleksandr Moroz/123RF; 10 (1f): Maksym Yemelyanov/123RF; 10 (2,1): Otnaydur/Shutterstock; 10 (2,2): Wavebreakmedia/Shutterstock; 10 (2,3): Antonio Diaz/123RF; 10 (2,4): Elena Elisseeva/Shutterstock; 10 (2,5): Rob Marmion/Shutterstock; 10 (2,6): Michaeljung/Shutterstock; 10 (2,7): Luca Bertolli/123RF; 10 (2,8): Pressmaster/Shutterstock.

Unit 2

Page 12 (2,1): Andresr/Shutterstock; 12 (2,2): Pixelheadphoto digitalskillet/Shutterstock; 12 (2,3): Hfng/123RF; 12 (2,4): Deborah Kolb/Shutterstock; 12 (2,5): Goodluz/Shutterstock; 18: Jakkarin Rongkankeaw/123RF; 19: Andre Luiz Moreira/Shutterstock; 20: Kudryashka/Shutterstock.

Unit 3

Page 21 (2a): Studio 8/Pearson Education Ltd; 21 (2b): Coleman Yuen/Pearson Education Asia Ltd; 21 (2c): Dmitry Kalinovsky/Shutterstock; 21 (2d): Iakov Filimonov/Shutterstock; 21 (2e): Dolgachov/123RF; 21 (2f): Ginasanders/123RF; 21 (2g): George Rudy/Shutterstock; 21 (2h): Kwangmoozaa/Shutterstock; 24 (1,1): Rido/123RF; 24 (1,2): Hurst Photo/Shutterstock; 24 (1,3): l i g h t p o e t/Shutterstock; 24 (1,4): PR Image Factory/Shutterstock; 24 (1,5): Stephen Coburn/Shutterstock; 26 (1,1): Felix Mizioznikov/Shutterstock; 26 (1,2): Jason Stitt/Shutterstock; 26 (1,3): IKO/123RF; 26 (1,4): 627505/Shutterstock; 28: Dotshock/Shutterstock; 29 (1): Vgstockstudio/Shutterstock; 29 (2): 36clicks/123RF; 29 (3): Pavel L Photo and Video/Shutterstock; 29 (4): Sirtravelalot/Shutterstock; 29 (5): Adisa/Shutterstock.

Library of Congress Cataloging-in-Publication Data

A catalog record for the print edition is available from the Library of Congress

Printed in Brazil by Reproset RPSZ 220086

ISBN-13: 978-0-13-683358-1

ScoutAutomatedPrintCode

pearsonenglish.com/connectivity

Unit 4
Page 30: Shutterstock; 31 (1): Ventdusud/Shutterstock; 31 (2): Vinicius Tupinamba/Shutterstock; 31 (3 left): Sylv1rob1/Shutterstock; 31 (3 right): Antonio Jorge Nunes/Shutterstock; 33: Zphoto/Shutterstock; 35 (1): Djomas/Shutterstock; 35 (2): Dragon Images/Shutterstock; 35 (3): Sofi photo/Shutterstock; 35 (4): Tracy Whiteside/Shutterstock; 35 (5): Roman Samborskyi/123RF; 36: Anemad/Shutterstock; 37: White Room/Shutterstock.

Unit 5
Page 40 (1): Kozlik/Shutterstock; 40 (2): Nd3000/123RF; 40 (3): Gpointstudio/Shutterstock; 40 (4): Stokkete/123RF; 40 (5): Matimix/Shutterstock; 40 (6): Syda Productions/Shutterstock; 43 (UK flag): Charnsitr/Shutterstock; 43 (salad): YanLev/Shutterstock; 43 (Mexico flag): Imageflow/123RF; 43 (Japan flag): Globe Turner/Shutterstock; 43 (background): Color Symphony/Shutterstock; 47 (1): Fun Way Illustration/Shutterstock; 47 (2): Kakigori Studio/Shutterstock; 47 (3): Anirban Sarkar/Pearson India Education Services Pvt. Ltd; 47 (4): Tynyuk/Shutterstock.

Unit 6
Page 48 (shoes): Lalouetto/Shutterstock; 48 (skit): Karkas/Shutterstock; 48 (jacket): Karkas/Shutterstock; 48 (t-shirt): Elenovsky/Shutterstock; 48 (tie): Artem Avetisyan/Shutterstock;48 (dress): Tarzhanova/123Rf; 48 (sweater): Karkas/Shutterstock; 48 (polo shirt): Ekkamai Chaikanta/Shutterstock; 48 (bottom): Kimberley McClard/Shutterstock; 51: Dean Drobot/Shutterstock; 53 (1): Vichy Deal/Shutterstock; 53 (2): StepStock/Shutterstock; 53 (3): Robyn Mackenzie/123RF; 53 (4): Vladimir Sazonov/Shutterstock; 53 (5): Veronica Louro/Shutterstock; 55 (dress): Vlad Teodor/Shutterstock; 55 (blouse): Evaletova/123RF; 55 (skirt): Karkas/Shutterstock; 55 (trousers): Jiang Zhongyan/Shutterstock; 55 (shirt): Tkemot/Shutterstock; 55 (tie): Terekhov igor/Shutterstock; 56 (1): Belchonock/123RF; 56 (2): Wilawan Khasawong/123RF; 56 (3): Viktorija Reuta/Shutterstock; 56 (4): Chiyacat/Shutterstock; 56 (Charlie): Brasoveanu George Bogdan/123RF; 56 (Claire): Indira's Work/Shutterstock.

Unit 7
Page 57 (1): Original photography by Sharon Hoogstraten and David Mager/Pearson Education; 57 (2): Miya227/Shutterstock; 57 (3): Lightfieldstudios/123RF; 57 (4): Original photography by Sharon Hoogstraten and David Mager/Pearson Education; 57 (5): Original photography by Sharon Hoogstraten and David Mager/Pearson Education; 57 (6): Friends Stock/Shutterstock; 57 (7): Ammentorp Photography/Shutterstock; 57 (8): Graphbottles/Shutterstock; 57 (9): Original photography by Sharon Hoogstraten and David Mager/Pearson Education; 58: Gareth Boden/Pearson Education Ltd; 59: Goir/Shutterstock; 61: Luis Louro/Shutterstock; 64: Dmitry_Tsvetkov/Shutterstock; 65 (1): David Gilder/Shutterstock; 65 (2): Goir/Shutterstock; 65 (3): Kostasgr/Shutterstock; 65 (4): Mike Flippo/Shutterstock.

Unit 8
Page 71 (1): Wavebreak Media Ltd/123RF; 71 (2): Fiphoto/123RF; 71 (3): Coleman Yuen/Pearson Education Asia Ltd; 71 (4): Manfred Steinbach123/RF; 71 (5): Jacek Chabraszewski/Shutterstock; 71 (6): Checubus/Shutterstock; 71 (7): Sorbis/Shutterstock; 71 (8): Shutterstock; 73: Qingqing/Shutterstock; 74 (1): Charles Brutlag/Shutterstock; 74 (2): Fransiska Indromojo/123RF; 74 (3): KKulikov/Shutterstock; 74 (4): Voronin76/Shutterstock; 74 (5): 5 second Studio/Shutterstock; 74 (6): Jfreeman/Shutterstock; 74 (7): SS1001/Shutterstock; 74 (8): Gts/Shutterstock.

Unit 9
Page 76 (1): Sagir/Shutterstock; 76 (2): TerraceStudio/Shutterstock; 76 (3): Pavel V Mukhin/Shutterstock; 76 (4): Mimo/Shutterstock; 76 (5): Mawielobob/123RF; 76 (6): SAKstock/Shutterstock; 79 (a): Soft_light/Shutterstock; 79 (b): Halfpoint/Shutterstock; 79 (c): Sirtravelalot/Shutterstock; 79 (d): Jacek Chabraszewski/Shutterstock; 79 (e): Iofoto/Shutterstock; 79 (f): Olga Danylenko/Shutterstock; 82: Daniel L Smith/Shutterstock; 83 (1): Tainar/Shutterstock; 83 (2): FotoKina/Shutterstock; 83 (3): Minerva Studio/Shutterstock; 83 (4): Sondem/123RF./

Unit 10
Page 84 (1): Tim UR/Shutterstock; 84 (2): Valentyn Volkov/Shutterstock; 84 (3): Photocrea/Shutterstock; 84 (4): Chikapylka/Shutterstock; 84 (5): Ian 2010/Shutterstock; 84 (6): Samokhin/Shutterstock; 84 (7): Africa Studio/Shutterstock; 84 (8): Peter Zijlstra/Shutterstock; 84 (9): Topseller/Shutterstock; 85 (1): Anmbph/123RF; 85 (2): Valentyn Volkov/Shutterstock; 85 (3): Pavlok/123RF; 85 (4): Oleksiy Mark/Shutterstock; 85 (5): Urfin/Shutterstock; 85 (6): ifong/Shutterstock; 86 (left): YanLev/Shutterstock; 86 (center): Dmitri Ma/Shutterstock; 86 (right): Fotografiche/Shutterstock; 87 (a): Angel Simon/Shutterstock; 87 (b): PixMarket/Shutterstock; 87 (c): Dmitriy Krasko/Shutterstock; 87 (d): Nikola Bilic/Shutterstock; 87 (e): Aaron Amat/Shutterstock; 87 (f): Margouillat photo/Shutterstock; 87 (g): Chones/Shutterstock; 87 (h): Tobi/123RF; 87 (i): Sommai Larkjit/123RF; 87 (j): Multiart/Shutterstock; 87 (k): Dani Vincek/Shutterstock; 87 (l): Rtstudio/Shutterstock; 89 (1): Barbro Bergfeldt/Shutterstock; 89 (2): Onemorebox/Shutterstock; 89 (3): Mariyana M/Shutterstock; 89 (4): Preto Perola/Shutterstock; 89 (5): Scanrail/123RF; 91 (1): Howard Sayer/Shutterstock; 91 (2): Akom Somsamai/Shutterstock; 91 (3): Ra3rn/Shutterstock; 91 (center): Jordi2r/123RF; 92 (1): Tim UR/Shutterstock; 92 (2): Maceofoto/Shutterstock; 92 (3): Topseller/Shutterstock; 92 (4): Iurii Kachkovskyi/Shutterstock; 92 (5): Tim UR/Shutterstock; 92 (6): Utima/123RF; 92 (7): Elena Schweitzer/Shutterstock; 92 (8): Utima/123RF.

Illustration Credits
Steve Attoe pp. 9, 44 (bottom); Kenneth Batelman pp. 24, 67; Leanne Franson pp. 7, 14, 31, 39 (top), 59; Brian Hughes pp. 25, 27 (left column), 39 (bottom); Stephen Hutchings p. 81; Robert Kemp p. 22 (top); Jim Kopp pp. 21, 27 (right column); Suzanne Mogensen pp. 33, 41; Janet Norquest p. 28; Dusan Petricic pp. 44 (top), 49, 50, 55, 75; Phil Scheuer pp. 58 (bottom), 60; Steve Schulman p. 52; Neil Stewart pp. 22 (bottom), 23, 68; Gary Torrisi pp. 13, 26, 66, 69; Anna Veltfort pp. 15, 58 (top).

CONTENTS

Welcome 1

UNIT 1　People and Occupations 3

UNIT 2　Personal Information 12

UNIT 3　Neighborhoods 21

UNIT 4　Families 30

UNIT 5　Time and Events 39

UNIT 6　Clothes 48

UNIT 7　Free Time and Chores 57

UNIT 8　Houses and Homes 66

UNIT 9　Activities and Plans 75

UNIT 10　Food and Drinks 83

Welcome

1 Look at the pictures. Write the correct direction from the box.

listen   practice with a partner   read   repeat   write

1 ....
2 .... 
3 ....

4 ....
5 ....

2 Label the classroom vocabulary in the pictures. Write the words from the box.

a board   a book   a chair   a desk   a notebook   a pen   a pencil   a table

1 ....   3 ....   5 ....   7 ....
2 ....   4 ....   6 ....   8 ....

3 Complete the conversation. Introduce yourself.

A: Hi, I'm Katharine.

YOU ....

A: Glad to meet you!

YOU ....

4 Complete the conversations. Write the correct greeting from the box.

Good afternoon   Good evening   Good morning

7:00 A.M.

1 **A:** .... , Misha!
  B: Hi, Veronica!

3:00 P.M.

2 **A:** ....
  Nice to meet you!
  B: Oh, hello! Nice to meet you, too!

7:00 P.M.

3 **A:** .... , Mr. Chen!
  B: Hi, Patrice. How's it going?

5 Complete the conversation with sentences from the box.

Bye, Manuel.   I'm fine.   Not bad, thanks. And you?
OK. See you!   See you later.

Manuel: Hi, Leticia. How are you?

Leticia: (1) ....

Manuel: (2) ....

*****

Manuel: Well, Good-bye.

Leticia: (3) ....

Manuel: (4) ....

Leticia: (5) ....

UNIT 1 People and Occupations

Warm-up

1 Look at the picture. Circle the correct subject pronoun.

1 (We / They / I) am Liz.
2 (He / She / You) is Anna.
3 (I / He / You) are students.

4 (He / We / She) are students.
5 (He / You / We) is Dave.
6 (They / I / She) are Marcus and Luna.

2 Complete the sentences with the correct pronouns from the box.

| He | I | She | They | We | you |

1 Hi, ………………. am Paul.
2 I am Sam and he is Theo. ………………. are Sam and Theo.
3 It's nice to meet ………………. , Sam and Theo.
4 ………………. is Lisa.
5 He is Bill and she is Angela. ………………. are Bill and Angela.
6 ………………. is John.

3 Match the occupations with the pictures. Write the letter on the line.

1 ………. a doctor
2 ………. a teacher
3 ………. a chef
4 ………. a musician
5 ………. a student
6 ………. a singer

a
b
c
d
e
f

UNIT 1   3

LESSON 1

1 Look at each picture. Circle the correct occupation.

1 (an artist / a photographer / a flight attendant)

2 (a flight attendant / a pilot / a scientist)

3 (an artist / a pilot / an athlete)

4 (an actor / a manager / a writer)

5 (a photographer / a manager / an engineer)

2 Complete the conversations with the correct occupations.

1 **A:** Is he ....?
   B: Yes, he is.

2 **A:** Is she ....?
   B: Yes, she is.

3 **A:** Is Martin a pilot?
   B: No, he's not. He's
   ....

4 **A:** Is Eleanor a chef?
   B: No, she's not. She's
   ....

5 **A:** Is Franco ....?
   B: Yes, he is.

3 Write statements with the verb be. Use contractions and articles.

1 I / not / flight attendant
   I'm not a flight attendant.

2 he / not / singer
   He's not a singer.

3 you / engineer
   You're an engineer.

4 you / not / musician
   You're not a musician.

5 he / not / artist
   He's not an artist.

6 she / teacher
   She's a teacher.

7 I / not / manager
   I'm not a manager.

8 he / actor
   He's an actor.

9 she / not / scientist
   She's not a scientist.

4 Write affirmative statements with the verb be. Use contractions, articles, and the occupations in parentheses.

1 A: What does he do?
   B: He's a manager. (manager)

2 A: What does she do?
   B: She's a pilot. (pilot)

3 A: What do you do?
   B: I'm a student. (student)

4 A: What does she do?
   B: She's a chef. (chef)

5 A: What does he do?
   B: He's an athlete. (athlete)

6 A: What do you do?
   B: I'm a teacher. (teacher)

7 A: What does he do?
   B: He's a photographer. (photographer)

8 A: What does she do?
   B: She's an artist. (artist)

9 A: What does he do?
   B: He's a flight attendant. (flight attendant)

5 Complete the conversation with sentences from the box.

| A chef?   Hi, Marijo. Nice to meet you.   Nice to meet you, too, Sev! |
| Sev's a chef.   Sev, this is Marijo. She's a singer.   Yes. I work at the Corso Cafe. |

Luka: (1) ....
Sev: (2) ....
Marijo: (3) ....
Luka: (4) ....
Marijo: (5) ....
Sev: (6) ....

UNIT 1

6 Complete the sentences in your own way. Write names.

1 .... is a famous artist.
2 .... is a famous musician.
3 .... is a famous writer.
4 My favorite singer is ....
5 My favorite actor is ....
6 My favorite athlete is ....

LESSON 2

1 Circle the correct words to complete the yes / no questions and short answers.

1 A: Is he a chef?
B: No, he (is / **isn't** / not). He's a manager.

2 A: (**Are you a** / You're / You are) musician?
B: Yes, I am.

3 A: Is Fiona a writer?
B: Yes, she (**'s** / is / writer).

4 A: (**Are Jenna and Ted** / Jenna and Ted / Jenna and Ted are) artists?
B: Yes, they are.

5 A: Are you a pilot?
B: Yes, I ('m / **am** / pilot).

6 A: (Are they / You / **Are you**) photographers?
B: Yes, we are.

7 A: Are they engineers?
B: Yes, they (**are** / engineers / 're).

8 A: (Is Michael a / **Is Michael an** / Michael is) scientist?
B: No, he's not. He's a doctor.

2 Complete the conversations. Use contractions when possible.

1 A: ......*Are*...... you Tim and Judy?
B: No, ...*we aren't*...... . We're Tom and Jen.

2 A: .... they Evan and Michael?
B: No, ... They're Louis and Jack.

3 A: .... he a doctor?
B: Yes, ...

4 A: .... you Ricardo?
B: Yes, ...

5 A: .... they scientists?
B: Yes, ...

6 A: .... you writers?
B: No, we .... We're photographers.

7 A: .... Ella?
B: No, she .... She's Lilian.

8 A: .... Philip a doctor?
B: No, ... not. He's an engineer.

9 A: .... students?
B: Yes, we ....

3 Circle the correct answer to complete the conversations. Circle the correct words.

1 A: They (**aren't** / isn't / am not) flight attendants.
B: They're pilots.

2 A: (They / **Are you** / Is he) doctors?
B: Yes, we are.

3 A: Are you and Taylor (musician / a musician / **musicians**)?
B: No, we're not.

4 A: Are they engineers?
B: No, (**they** / they're / you) aren't.

5 A: Are you chefs?
B: Yes, (we're / **we are** / we aren't).

6 A: Are you (artist / artists / **an artist**)?
B: Yes, I am.

7 A: (**Are they** / Is he / Are we) managers?
B: No, they're writers.

8 A: Are you and Andrea engineers?
B: Yes, (we're / **we are** / you are).

4 Complete each conversation. Use the correct forms of the words in parentheses. Use contractions when possible.

1 A: *Are you managers* ?
   (you / be / managers)
   B: Yes, we are.

2 A: .... ?
   (they / be / athlete)
   B: Yes, they are.

3 A: We ....
   (be / not / singer)
   B: Are you photographers?

4 A: .... ?
   (be / you / scientist)
   B: No, we aren't. We're writers.

5 A: .... ?
   (be / you / chef)
   B: Yes, I am.

6 A: They ....
   (be / not / actor)
   B: Are you singers?

7 A: They aren't pilots.
   B: .... ?
   (be / they / flight attendant)

8 A: .... ?
   (be / they / musician)
   B: No, they're not. They're actors.

9 A: Are you students?
   B: No, we aren't.
   ....
   (we / be / teacher)

5 Circle the correct words to complete the conversation.

A: (1) (Excuse me / Thank you / You're welcome). Are you Ben?

B: No, (2) (he isn't / I'm not / I am). I'm Simon. That's Ben.

A: (3) (Are you Simon? / Where? / Is he Simon?)

B: Right over there.

A: Oh. Thank you.

B: (4) (Excuse me / Thank you / You're welcome).

6 Read the list. Then look at the pictures and complete the conversation.

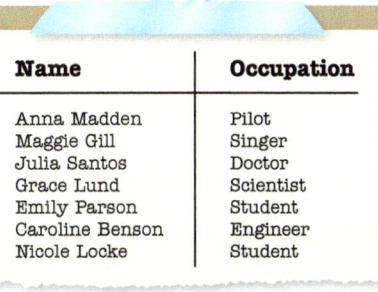

Name	Occupation
Anna Madden	Pilot
Maggie Gill	Singer
Julia Santos	Doctor
Grace Lund	Scientist
Emily Parson	Student
Caroline Benson	Engineer
Nicole Locke	Student

Are you Maggie?

1 ....

Are you Anna?

2 ....

Are you Caroline?

3 ....

Are you Emily and Nicole?

4 ....

LESSON 3

1 Circle the correct capitalization to complete each statement or question.

1. He is a (**Pilot** / **pilot**).
2. Is Yoko from (**Japan** / **japan**)?
3. They are (**Scientists** / **scientists**).
4. Excuse me. Are you (**Luis** / **luis**)?
5. Are you from (**Portugal** / **portugal**)?
6. I am a (**Singer** / **singer**).
7. Are they (**Musicians** / **musicians**)?
8. She is from (**New York City** / **new york city**).

2 Complete the sentences with the nouns in parentheses. Begin each proper noun with a capital letter.

1. My name is ....*Sarah*............ . (sarah)
2. Mr. Browne is a .... (chef)
3. He is from .... (mexico)
4. Is .... an athlete? (alexandra)
5. The .... is in the classroom. (teacher)
6. .... is a writer. (sean williams)
7. Are you from .... ? (china)
8. Is Philip a .... ? (doctor)
9. Sophia and .... are from Italy. (laura)

3 Read the occupations in the box. Count the syllables. Write each occupation in the correct place on the chart.

actor   athlete   chef   ~~engineer~~   manager   musician   photographer   scientist   singer   writer

1 syllable	2 syllables	3 syllables	4 syllables
		engineer	

4 Complete the conversation with sentences from the box. There are three extra sentences.

And you are?   Excuse me?   How do you spell that?   P-E-T-E-R
Thanks!   Where?   You're welcome.

A: Hello, I'm Peter Mason.
B: (1) ....
A: Peter Mason.
B: (2) ....
A: (3) .... M-A-S-O-N.
B: (4) OK. ....

DID YOU KNOW...?
People today hold more jobs over their lifetimes than their great-grandparents did. Studies show that, on average, people have 11.7 jobs between age 18–48. About 27% of these people have 15 jobs or more, while 10% percent held 0–4 jobs.

LESSON 4

1 Take the quiz. What do we learn about the people? Circle the correct letter.

a the names of their friends b their occupations c the names of their family members

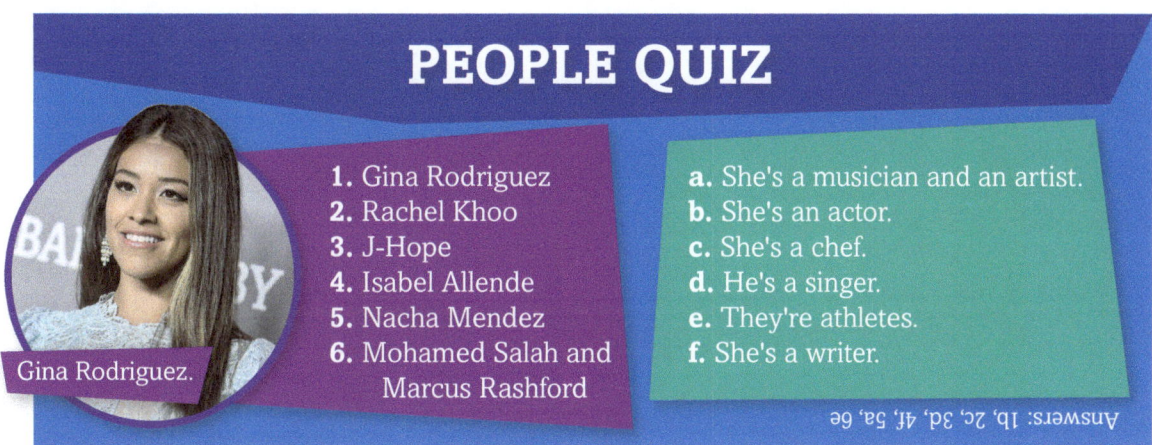

PEOPLE QUIZ

Gina Rodriguez.

1. Gina Rodriguez
2. Rachel Khoo
3. J-Hope
4. Isabel Allende
5. Nacha Mendez
6. Mohamed Salah and Marcus Rashford

a. She's a musician and an artist.
b. She's an actor.
c. She's a chef.
d. He's a singer.
e. They're athletes.
f. She's a writer.

Answers: 1b, 2c, 3d, 4f, 5a, 6e

2 Complete the sentences about the people in Exercise 1.

1 Gina Rodriguez .... a singer. She's an ....
2 Are Mohamed Salah and J-Hope actors? ....
3 Rachel Khoo and J-Hope .... writers. She .... a chef, and he .... a singer.
4 Is Isabel Allende a writer? ....
5 Are Mohamed Salah and Marcus Rashford athletes? ....
6 Rashford and Rodriguez .... chefs. He .... an athlete, and she .... an actor.
7 Is Nacha Mendez a chef? ....
8 Nacha Mendez is a .... and an ....

3 Look at the picture. Write an affirmative and a negative statement about the people. Use contractions.

1 *She's an artist. She's not a pilot.* 4 ....
2 .... 5 ....
3 .... 6 ....

UNIT 1 9

VOCABULARY EXPANDER

1 Match each occupation with a picture. Write the letter on the line.

1 .... a gardener
2 .... a mechanic
3 .... a veterinarian
4 .... a server / a waiter
5 .... a reporter
6 .... a hairdresser

a 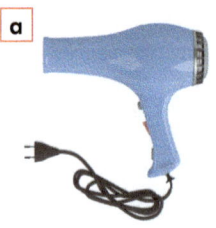 b 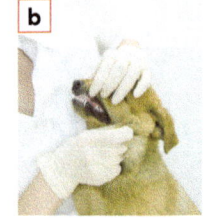 c

d  e  f

2 Look at the pictures. Write a statement about each person's occupation. Use <u>He</u> or <u>She</u> and the verb <u>be</u>.

1 .... 2 .... 3 ....

4 .... 4 .... 6 ....

7 .... 8 ....

GUIDED WRITING

Write one affirmative and one negative sentence about five people you know. Begin sentences with a capital letter.

Gail isn't a chef. She's a student.

JUST FOR FUN

1 Read the statements. Then write an occupation for each person.

A RIDDLE FOR YOU!

Ms. Adams, Ms. Baker, Ms. Cullen, and Ms. Dare have four different occupations—engineer, architect, doctor, and scientist (but NOT in that order).

Ms. Adams and Ms. Cullen are not doctors. Ms. Cullen and Ms. Dare are not architects.

Ms. Baker and Ms. Cullen are not scientists. Ms. Adams is not a scientist.

Ms. Adams: .... Ms. Cullen: ....
Ms. Baker: .... Ms. Dare: ....

Look across and down. Circle the eight occupations. Then write the occupations on the lines.

1 ....
2 ....
3 ....
4 ....
5 ....
6 ....
7 ....
8 ....

```
N E I M E P A E N N B K R P P E
M O E T E O A M E S U I H A T L
A E L P O L L H N C N N N T R Y
N T W E S A A S A I H H R R L I
A O R H T E T T R E T E T E N C
G K I E N P H E S N A H N E S A
E N T P C R L A M T R E N S R E
R T E A E A E I N I N N E R N U
K A R A S H T A A S E R E R A T
O A T N Y T E I U T E H G R N M
E C P H O T O G R A P H E R H E
R T N A S M B E N G I N E E R B
N O E N R A E E E E R A E R E L
A R O K P E G N E R A N U U H E
O T T A R T I S T T L E G C T E
N N K R N N E R N R T B I G E T
```

UNIT 1 11

UNIT 2 Personal Information

Warm-up

1 Look at the underlined word in each sentence. Is it a title, a first name, or a last name? Circle the correct answer.

1 Mr. Daniel <u>Le</u> (title / first name / last name)
2 Mrs. <u>Whitney</u> Grayson (title / first name / last name)
3 <u>Mr.</u> Rick Trudeau (title / first name / last name)
4 Ms. <u>LaVondra</u> French (title / first name / last name)
5 <u>Miss</u> Edith Knowles (title / first name / last name)
6 Mr. Charles <u>Lott</u> (title / first name / last name)

2 Look at each picture. Write the correct title.

1 .... Annie Ray

2 .... Tracey Albracht

3 .... Lu Chen

4 .... Samantha Sherman

5 .... Brown

3 Complete the conversations with the correct titles.

1 **A:** Did you meet the new couple next door?
  B: Yes, I did. I met Mr. and .... Ramirez yesterday.

2 **A:** I heard that the new English teacher is very handsome.
  B: .... Walters? I guess he is. He's really nice, too.

3 **A:** How was your appointment with your new doctor?
  B: It went well.
  A: Did you like her?
  B: Yes. .... Adams was very helpful.

4 **A:** I'd like to introduce you to my little sister, Susie.
  B: Well, hi .... Susie. It's nice to meet you.

4 Match the contact information on the left with the phrase on the right. Draw a line.

1 tlane1962@att.net
2 252 Cherry Lane, Nashotah, Wisconsin 53058
3 914-555-3070

a a phone number
b an e-mail address
c an address

5 Complete the address book. Write information for three people you know.

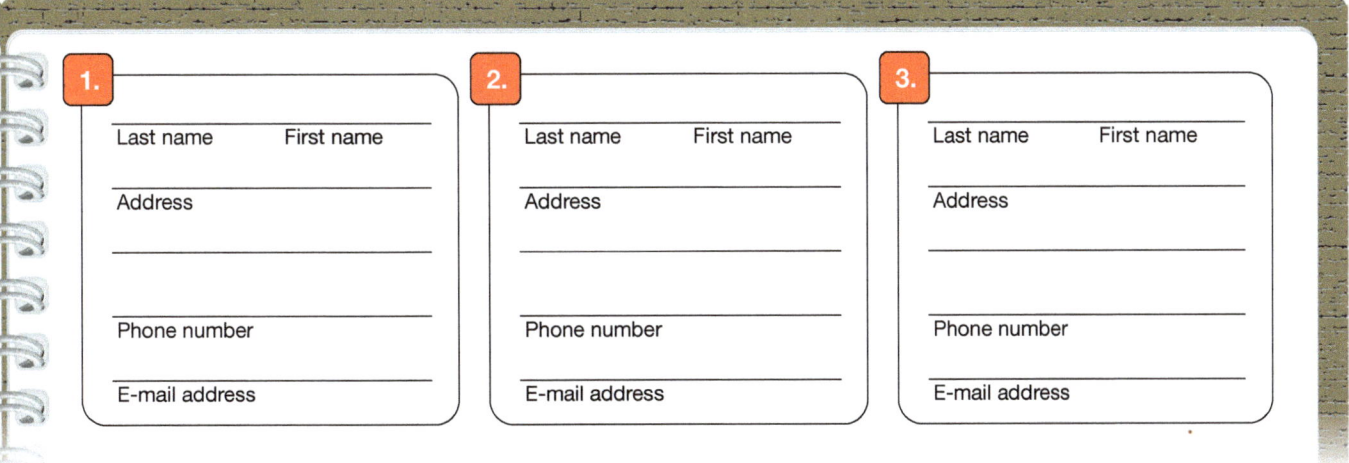

LESSON 1

1 Look at each picture. What is the people's relationship? Write words from the box. One choice isn't used.

a boss   a classmate   a colleague   a friend   a neighbor   a teammate

1 ....
2 ....
3 ....
4 ....
5 ....

2 Look at the pictures. Write possessive adjectives.

1 Mr. Huang is .... boss.

2 .... doctor is Dr. Mason.

3 .... neighbors are Mr. and Mrs. Hernandez.

4 Ms. Jalbert is .... teacher.

3 Complete the sentences. Circle the correct words.

1 Are .... Mr. Eddie's students?
   a they   b their   c our

2 Wayne and Amanda are .... colleagues.
   a I   b he   c my

3 We are .... friends.
   a her   b our   c she

4 .... am their boss.
   a They   b I   c My

5 .... are my neighbors.
   a He   b She   c They

6 Truman and Bradley are .... teammates.
   a he's   b his   c he

4 Look at the pictures. Complete the sentences about relationships with possessive nouns.

1 She is .... Lucy's friend ....

2 He is ....

3 He is ....

4 They are ....

5 Complete the conversation. Use sentences from the box.

| Hello, Gerry | Hi, Elaine | Nice to meet you, too | this is Gerry |

Fred: Elaine, **(1)** .... Gerry's my classmate.

Elaine: **(2)** ....

Fred: Elaine is one of my neighbors.

Gerry: **(3)** .... Nice to meet you.

Elaine: **(4)** ....

LESSON 2

1 Write the numbers as words. Use words from the box. Two words are not used.

| eight | four | one | seven | sixteen | ten | thirteen | twenty | zero |

1 0 ....
2 4 ....
3 7 ....
4 10 ....
5 13 ....
6 16 ....
7 20 ....

UNIT 2 15

2 Do the math. Write the answers in words.

1 two + six = ...
2 ten − five = ...
3 fifteen − fourteen = ...
4 three + eight = ...
5 twelve + seven = ...
6 twenty − sixteen = ...

3 Circle the correct word or words to complete each conversation.

1 **A:** (What's / What / What are) your phone number?
   B: 212-555-2431.
2 **A:** (What's / What / What are) their favorite colors?
   B: Blue and purple.
3 **A:** (What's / What / What are) is your last name?
   B: Jenkins. J-E-N-K-I-N-S.
4 **A:** (What's / What / What are) your address?
   B: 305 Major Street.
5 **A:** (What's / What / What are) Mr. Wright's first name?
   B: I think it's George.

4 Look at the business cards. Read the responses. Then write questions with **What's**. Use possessive nouns or possessive adjectives.

1 **A:** ......*What's Mr. Silver's first name*...... ?   **B:** Jeff.
2 **A:** ......*What's his e-mail address*...... ?   **B:** jeff.silver@edi.com.
3 **A:** .... ?   **B:** He's an engineer.
4 **A:** .... ?   **B:** 0208 755 8050.
5 **A:** .... ?   **B:** 77 York St.
6 **A:** .... ?   **B:** (612) 9262-1036.
7 **A:** .... ?   **B:** She's an architect.
8 **A:** .... ?   **B:** 215 East 11th Street.

5 Complete the conversation with sentences from the box. Two choices are not used.

| And what's your address? | Garcia. | My first name? Shana. | That's right. |
| What's your email address? | What's your occupation? | 321-5207. |

A: What's your last name, please?

B: **(1)** ....

A: And your first name?

B: **(2)** ....

A: Great. **(3)** ....

B: It's 555 Overview Court.

A: Overview Court?

B: **(4)** ....

A: Great. **(5)** ....

B: It's sgarcia@email.com.

LESSON 3

1 Complete the conversation with words from the box.

| Are | I am | I'm | I'm from | is | isn't | We're | Where | Where's |

A: Hey. **(1)** .... Brad, and this is my friend, Lyle. **(2)** .... from Boston.

B: Hi. I'm Skylar. Nice to meet you.

A: Nice to meet you, too. **(3)** .... are you from, Skylar?

B: **(4)** .... Puerto Rico.

A: **(5)** .... you from San Juan?

B: Yes, **(6)** .... Good guess.

A: **(7)** .... your friend from?

B: Oh, Camila? She's from Argentina.

A: **(8)** .... she from Buenos Aires?

B: No, she **(9)** .... She's from La Plata.

2 Complete the conversations with be from. Use contractions when possible.

1 **A:** ....Are they........ from Berlin?
   B: No, ...they aren't...... . They're from Potsdam.

2 **A:** Where .... from?
   B: I'm .... Lansing, Michigan.

3 **A:** .... your mother .... Seoul?
   B: No, she isn't. .... Hong Kong.

4 **A:** .... you and your colleagues ....?
   B: .... Montreal, Canada.

5 **A:** .... from Mexico City?
   B: Yes, ...

6 **A:** .... he from?
   B: .... from South Africa.

7 **A:** Where .... from?
   B: She .... Italy.

UNIT 2 17

3 Complete the conversation with words from the box. Two phrases are not used.

| How do you spell that | No, she isn't | Right over there | Thanks | that's my colleague |
| What's your occupation | Where are you from | Your address | Your name | |

A: (1) ...., please?

B: Sure. It's Quincy Davis.

A: (2) .... ?

B: Q-U-I-N-C-Y D-A-V-I-S.

A: (3) ...., Mr. Davis?

B: I'm from Sydney. Oh, and (4) ...., Sue Shore.
(5) ....

A: Is Ms. Shore from Sydney, too?

B: (6) .... She's from Dallas, Texas.

A: Got it. (7) ....

B: You're welcome.

LESSON 4

1 Match the countries on the left with the nationalities on the right. Draw a line.

1 Kendra is from Brazil.
2 We're from Canada.
3 He's from China.
4 I'm from Japan.
5 She's from Mexico.
6 They're from the U.K.
7 Bo is from the U.S.
8 I'm from Italy.
9 He's from Columbia.
10 She's from Russia.
11 We're from France.
12 Tatiana is from Spain.

a They're British.
b He's American.
c She's Mexican.
d He's Chinese.
e We're Canadian.
f I'm Japanese.
g She's Brazilian.
h He's Columbian.
i She's Spanish.
j We're French.
k She's Russian.
l I'm Italian.

DID YOU KNOW…?

The city with the longest name in the world is Thailand's capital, Bangkok. Its full name is:

Krung Thep Mahanakhon Amon Rattanakosin Mahinthara Yuthaya Mahadilok Phop Noppharat Ratchathani Burirom Udomratchaniwet Mahasathan Amon Piman Awatan Sathit Sakkathattiya Witsanukam Prasit

2 Take the quiz. What do we learn about the famous people? Circle the correct answer.

a their contact information
b their occupations and nationalities
c the names of their family members

WHERE ARE THEY FROM?

 AKB48 are a famous pop band. They have 48 singers! Where are they from? _____

 Donny Pangilinan is a singer, but that's not all. He's also an actor and an athlete. What's his nationality? _____

 Rafaela Silva is an Olympic athlete. Where is she from? _____

4 Stephanie Sigman is an actor. She's from Ciudad Obregón. What's her nationality? _____

5 Jared Leto is a famous actor. He's also a singer and a photographer. Where is he from? _____

Answers: 1. Tokyo, Japan 2. Philippines 3. Brazil 4. Mexican 5. United States

3 Read about the people in Exercise 2 again. Circle the correct word to complete each statement.

1 AKB48's (occupation / nationality) is Japanese.
2 Rafaela Silva is (Brazilian / Brazil)?
3 Donny Pangilinan is a singer and (an actor / a photographer).
4 Is Mr. Pangilinan (Philippines / Filipino)? Yes, he is.
5 Stephanie Sigman is from Ciudad (Obregón / Mexico).
6 Ms. Sigman's occupation is (a singer / an actor).
7 Jared Leto is (American / Mexican).
8 Mr. Leto is (a photographer / in a band).

UNIT 2   19

VOCABULARY EXPANDER

Complete each conversation with Doctor, Captain, or Professor.

1. **A:** Hi. I'm Daria Gleason. I'm your pilot today.
   B: Nice to meet you, ... Gleason.

2. **A:** Good morning, class. Please open your textbooks to Chapter 3.
   B: Excuse me, ... Stevens. What page is that?
   A: Page 54.

3. **A:** My name is Tim Reid.
   B: Are you a nurse?
   A: No, I'm a doctor.
   B: Well, it's a pleasure to meet you, ... Reid.

GUIDED WRITING

Interview a friend. Ask questions about his or her personal information. Then use the information to write six sentences about that person. Begin each sentence with a capital letter. End with a period (.).

His first name is Tyler, and his last name is Cruz. He's from . . .

Ask about:
first name
last name
nationality
occupation
address
phone number
email address

JUST FOR FUN

Write the next number in words.

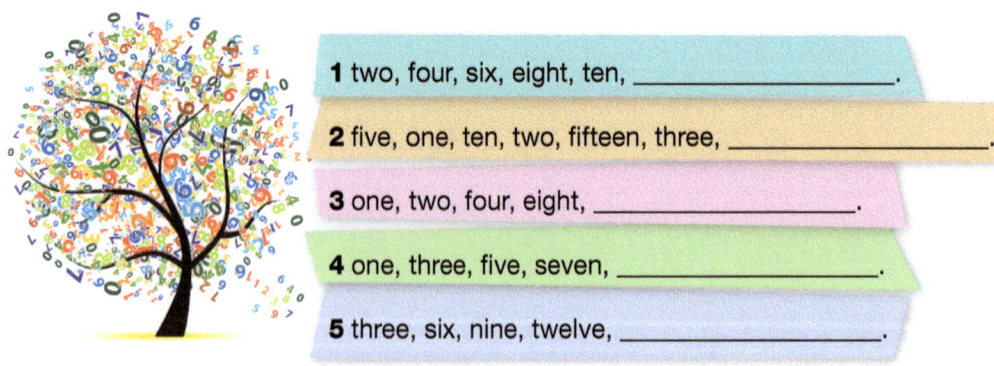

1 two, four, six, eight, ten, _____.
2 five, one, ten, two, fifteen, three, _____.
3 one, two, four, eight, _____.
4 one, three, five, seven, _____.
5 three, six, nine, twelve, _____.

UNIT 3 Neighborhoods

Warm-up

1 Look at the pictures. Circle the correct means of transportation to complete the conversations.

1 **A:** What is it?
   B: It's (a train / a car / a moped).

2 **A:** Is it (a motorcycle / a bicycle / a taxi)?
   B: Yes, it is.

3 **A:** Is it a car?
   B: No, it's (a subway / a train / a bus).

4 **A:** What is it?
   B: It's (a moped / a car / a bicycle).

5 **A:** Is it (a motorcycle / a subway / a taxi).
   B: Yes, it is!

6 **A:** It is not a moped.
   B: No, it's (a bicycle / a motorcycle / a taxi).

7 **A:** What is that?
   B: (A train / A car / A bus).

8 **A:** What is that? Is it a bicycle?
   B: No, it's not a bicycle. It's (a moped / a subway / a bus).

2 Match the places with the pictures. Write the letter on the line.

1 .... a bank
2 .... a restaurant
3 .... a gas station
4 .... a pharmacy
5 .... a supermarket
6 .... a school
7 .... a bus stop
8 .... a bookstore

3 Write the names of places in your neighborhood.

1 a restaurant: ....
2 a bookstore: ....
3 a pharmacy: ....
4 a school: ....
5 a bank: ....

LESSON 1

1 Look at each picture. Where is the house? Complete the location.

1 on the ....*left*.... 2 .... the corner 3 on the .... 4 .... the street

5 .... the street 6 .... the bank 7 .... the bookstore and the bank

2 Look at the picture. Match the places with the locations. Draw a line.

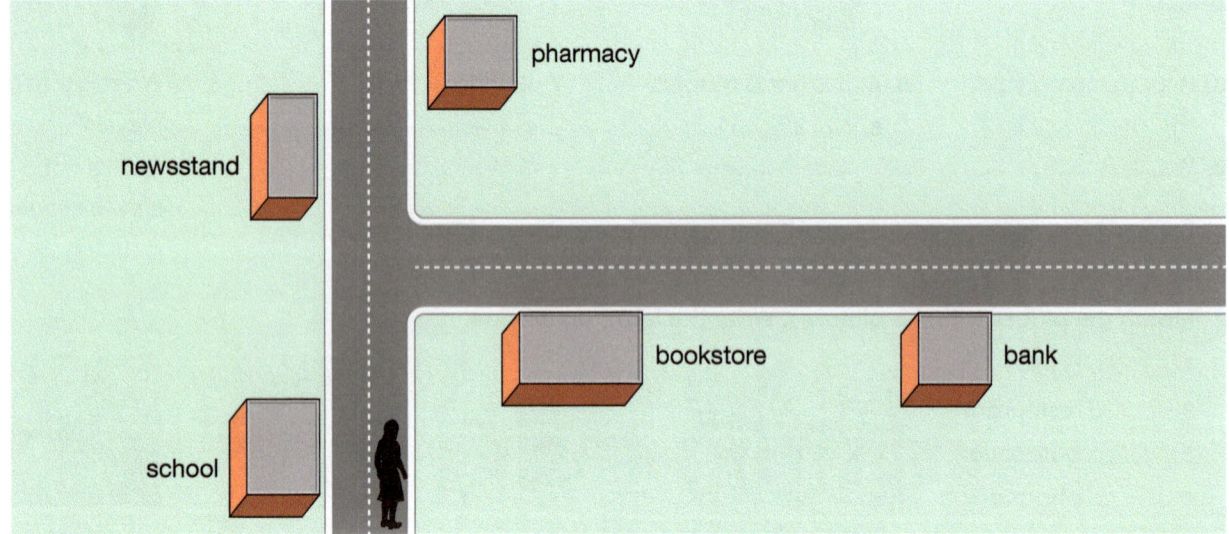

1 The bank is   a down the street on the right.
2 The pharmacy is   b around the corner.
3 The school is   c across the street.
4 The newsstand is   d next to the bookstore.
5 The bookstore is   e down the street on the left.

3 Put the words in order to make sentences.

1 bank / the / Where's
........Where's the bank............?

2 around / It's / corner / the
....

3 pharmacy / Where's / the
....?

4 It's / the / bank / between / and the bookstore
....

5 restaurant / is / Where / the
....?

6 next / the / to / It's / school
....

7 Where / bookstore / the / is
....?

8 between / and the restaurant / It's / the newsstand
....

9 the / It's / right / on
....

4 Write the correct word or words to complete the conversations. Use contractions.

1 **A:** Excuse me. ....Where's........ the bank?
  B: It's down the street, on the right.

2 **A:** Excuse me. .... Ben & Marty's Restaurant?
  B: Ben & Marty's? .... around the corner.

3 **A:** Excuse me. .... the .... ?
  B: The pharmacy? It's down the street, next to the bank.

4 **A:** Excuse me. .... Franklin Middle School?
  B: It's down the street and around the corner.

5 **A:** .... Where's the newsstand?
  B: .... ? It's across the street.

6 **A:** Excuse me. Where's the bookstore?
  B: .... next .... Ben & Marty's Restaurant.

7 **A:** Excuse me. .... ?
  B: The bank? It's down the ....

8 **A:** Excuse me. Where's the Good News Restaurant?
  B: .... down the street .... the left.

9 **A:** Excuse me. .... the pharmacy?
  B: .... across the street, between the school .... the bank.

5 Look at the pictures. Write questions and answers. Follow the model.

1 school

2 bookstore

3 pharmacy / restaurant / bank

4 newsstand

1 **A:** ....Where's the school........ ? **B:** ....It's around the corner........ .
2 **A:** .... ? **B:** ....
3 **A:** .... ? **B:** ....
4 **A:** .... ? **B:** ....

UNIT 3 23

6 How does the second speaker respond? Complete the conversation with sentences from the box.

| It's next to the gas station. On the left | The gas station? It's down the street | You're welcome |

A: Excuse me. Where's the gas station?
B: (1) ....
A: Thanks! And where's the bank?
B: (2) ....
A: Thanks again!
B: (3) ....

LESSON 2

1 Look at the pictures. Write the correct ways to get places on the line. Use words from the box.

| drive   take a taxi   take the bus   take the train   walk |

1 ....   2 ....   3 ....

4 ....   5 ....

2 Look at the pictures. Suggest how to get places. Complete the instructions. Use a capital letter at the beginning of a sentence.

1 <u>Take the train</u> to work.

2 The bookstore is down the street. Don't ....

3 The supermarket is around the corner on the right. ....

4 The pharmacy is next to the bookstore. ....

5 The school is around the corner. Don't ....

24   UNIT 3

3 Circle the correct answer to complete the conversations.

1 **A:** Can I take a bus to the pharmacy?
   B: Yes. (Drive / Take / Walk) the number 10 bus.

2 **A:** Can I walk to the newsstand?
   B: Take a bus. (Don't walk / Not walk / You don't walk).

3 **A:** Can I take a bus to the bookstore?
   B: The bookstore? It's around the corner. (No bus / Walk / You walk).

4 **A:** Can I take a bus to the school?
   B: No. (Don't / Drive / Take) the train.

5 **A:** Can I drive to the restaurant?
   B: (Don't drive / No drive / You don't drive). Walk.

6 **A:** Can I take a taxi to the restaurant?
   B: (Don't take / No / No take) a taxi. Take the bus.

7 **A:** Can I walk to the bank?
   B: (Take a taxi / Taxi / You take a taxi).

8 **A:** Can I take a train to the school?
   B: Yes. (Don't / Drive / Take) to the train station and take a train to the school.

4 Look at the pictures. Write the correct words to complete the instructions. Use contractions.

1 *Don't drive* to the restaurant.

2 .... to the school.

3 .... to the pharmacy.

4 .... to the bank.

5 .... to the restaurant.

6 .... to the bank.

7 .... to the pharmacy.

5 Write the sentences in the box in the correct order to complete the conversation.

And what about the post office?   Can I walk to the newsstand?   OK. Thanks!
Take the bus.   The newsstand? Sure.   The post office? No. Don't walk.

A: (1) ....
B: (2) ....
A: (3) ....
B: (4) ....
B: (5) ....
A: (6) ....

6 Tell a new classmate how to go places from school. Use an affirmative and a negative imperative.

1 to a bookstore: ....
2 to a bank: ....
3 to a pharmacy: ....
4 to a restaurant: ....

LESSON 3

1 Look at the pictures. Answer the questions. Use a <u>by</u> phrase from the box.

I take a bus to school.

1 How does she go to school?
....

I take a taxi to the bookstore.

2 How does he go to the bookstore?
....

I take the subway home.

3 How does she go home?
....

We take a train to work.

4 How do they go to work?
....

2 Look at each picture. Write the destination.

1 go ....

2 go ....

3 go ....

3 Look at the chart. Then match the names and statements. Draw a line.

NAME	DESTINATION	MEANS OF TRANPORTATION
Linda	house	taxi
Ali	briefcase/laptop	subway
Suki	book	bus
Anita	briefcase/laptop	motorcycle
Mike	books	bicycle
Fran	book	car
David	house	moped
Harry	briefcase/laptop	train

1 Linda   a I go to school by bicycle.
2 Ali   b I go to work by motorcycle.
3 Suki   c I go to school by bus.
4 Anita   d I go home by taxi.
5 Mike   e I go to work by subway.
6 Fran   f I go to work by train.
7 David   g I go to school by car.
8 Harry   h I go home by moped.

DID YOU KNOW . . . ?
Top 10 Best Public Transportation Systems

	Location	Name of System
1	Singapore	Mass Rapid Transit, or MRT
2	London	London Underground, or the Tube
3	Hong Kong	Mass Transit Railway, or MTR
4	Paris	Paris Métro
5	Madrid	Madrid Metro
6	Chicago	Chicago Transit Authority, or CTA
7	Tokyo	Tokyo Metro and Toei Subway
8	Dubai	Dubai Metro
9	Shanghai	Shanghai Metro
10	Zurich	Zurich Transport Network, or ZVV

4 Complete the conversation with words from the box. Two choices are not used.

> By taxi   Excuse me   go to work   How's it going   I drive
> Me   Pretty good   subway   What about you

A: Hey, Matt! **(1)** .... ?

B: **(2)** .... And you, Gina?

A: Fine, Matt, how do you **(3)** .... ?

B: By bus. **(4)** .... ?

A: **(5)** .... ? **(6)** ....

A: How do you go downtown?

B: **(7)** ....

LESSON 4

1 Look at each picture. Complete the sentences with the correct location or direction from the box.

across from   and   around the corner from   between   down the street from   on the right side

1 It's ....
of the street.

2 It's ....
the museum.

3 It's ....
the park.

4 It's ....
Main Street ....
Mercer Avenue.

5 It's ....
the theater.

2 Read the email. What is the message mainly about? Circle the correct answer.

a their family members   b their new neighborhood   c their occupations

From: Haley
To: Alyssa
Subject: I love Austin, Texas!

Inbox - Tuesday, November 13 at 9:12 AM
Details

Hi, Alyssa!

How are you? Marcus and I are doing fine. We love our new apartment in Austin, Texas. It's so great here! The supermarket is just across the street, and there's a bus stop around the corner from our building, so we can take the bus to the city. And Marcus's restaurant is just down the street, so he can walk to work. I take the bus to work, or I go by car with my neighbor Tony. He works in the same bookstore. There is a bank, a pharmacy, and a convenience store right down the street. How great is that?

How about you? How's school? Write!

xo Haley

3 Read the email in Exercise 2 again. Circle the correct word to complete each sentence.

1. Haley and Marcus take (the bus / the subway) to the city.
2. Haley and Tony work in a (restaurant / bookstore).
3. Haley takes (a taxi / the bus) to work, or she goes (by car / by moped).
4. The supermarket is (across / down) the street.
5. Marcus works in a (restaurant / bank).
6. The bank is right (down / across) the street.
7. Marcus (drives / walks) to work.
8. The pharmacy is (around the corner / down the street).

VOCABULARY EXPANDER

1 Look at the pictures. Write the place on the line.

a dry cleaners   a hotel   a shoe store   a tourist office   a toy store

1 ....
2 ....
3 ....
4 ....
5 ....

GUIDED WRITING

Write three questions about your neighborhood. Use the ideas as a guide. Then answer the questions. Describe the locations of the places. Begin each new sentence with a capital letter. End with a period.

Where's the restaurant? The restaurant is next to the bank.
It's . . .

Ideas
restaurant
bus stop
bookstore
transportation
(your own idea)

UNIT 3

UNIT 4 Families

Warm-up

1 Look at the picture. Match the names on the left with the family relationships on the right. Draw a line.

1 Alan and Theresa   a Tommy's grandfather
2 Molly   b Molly's father
3 Tommy   c Tommy's parents
4 Martina and Robert   d Molly's grandmother
5 Theresa   e Tommy's grandparents
6 Alan   f Molly's mother
7 Martina   g Martina's grandson
8 Robert   h Tommy's sister
9 Tommy and Molly   i Robert's grandchildren

2 Look at the picture in Exercise 1 again. Check <u>True</u> or <u>False</u>.

	True	False
1 Alan is Theresa's husband.	☐	☐
2 Tommy is Molly's brother.	☐	☐
3 Robert is Alan's son.	☐	☐
4 Theresa is Molly's mother.	☐	☐
5 Molly is Robert's grandson.	☐	☐
6 Molly is Alan's wife.	☐	☐
7 Tommy and Molly are Theresa's children.	☐	☐
8 Molly and Tommy are Martina's grandchildren.	☐	☐
9 Alan and Theresa are Robert's grandchildren.	☐	☐

LESSON 1

1 Circle the correct question to complete the conversations.

1. **A:** (Who's he / Who's she / Who are they)?
   B: He's my father.
2. **A:** (Who's he / Who's she / Who are they)?
   B: She's my grandmother.
3. **A:** (Who's he / Who's she / Who are they)?
   B: They're my cousins.
4. **A:** (Who's he / Who's she / Who are they)?
   B: She's my sister, Jada.
5. **A:** (Who's he / Who's she / Who are they)?
   B: They're my children.
6. **A:** (Who's he / Who's she / Who are they)?
   B: He's my grandson, Zack.

2 Complete the conversation. Write <u>What</u>, <u>Where</u>, or <u>Who</u>.

1. **Alex:** ....'s that?
   Malia: That's my grandparent's farm.
2. **Alex:** ....'s that?
   Malia: That's my sister.
3. **Alex:** ....'s you sister's first name?
   Malia: Gloria.
4. **Alex:** ....'s that?
   Malia: My grandfather.
5. **Alex:** .... are your parents?
   Malia: Over here, next to my brother.
6. **Alex:** ....'s his name?
   Malia: Martin.

3 Look at the pictures. Circle the correct answer to complete the conversation.

1. He's (old / short / tall), and she's (short / old / tall).

2. The child's grandmother is (old / young / short). The child is (old / tall / young).

3. They are (handsome / good-looking / pretty). She's (handsome / good-looking / pretty). He's (handsome / good-looking / pretty).

4 Read the sentences. Complete the conversations with the correct adjectives from the box. Two words are not used.

cute   good-looking   handsome   old   pretty   short   tall   young

1 **A:** Who's baby is that?
   B: It's Erica's. Isn't he ....?
2 **A:** Is your sister tall for her age?
   B: No, she's not. She's ....
3 **A:** Have you seen Candace's husband?
   B: I have. I noticed him right away. He's quite ....
4 **A:** Who are the .... people in this photo?
   B: Those are my cousins. They do look good.
5 **A:** Your grandmother looks so ....
   B: Yes, she does. She's not very old.
6 **A:** Your son is so ....
   B: Yes, he is. He's taller than his father.

5 Unscramble the words to write sentences.
1 sister / tall / is / Her / very   *Her sister is very tall*.
2 parents / very / My / short / are ....
3 brother's / My / really / wife / pretty / is ....
4 Todd / Jill / so / are / good-looking / and ....
5 a / very / man / handsome / He's ....
6 old / very / are / His / grandparents ....

6 Describe five relatives. Write complete sentences. Use adjectives and the adverbs <u>very</u>, <u>really</u>, and <u>so</u>.

My sister is very cute!

....
....
....
....
....

7 Complete the conversation with sentences from the box.

And is that your sister?   He's very handsome.   Oh, that's my brother. He's an athlete.
Who's that?   Wow! She's so tall!   Yes, he is.   Yes, she's a pilot.

A: (1) ....
B: (2) ....
A: (3) ....
B: (4) ....
A: (5) ....
B: (6) ....
A: (7) ....

LESSON 2

1 Complete the conversations. Write a subject pronoun + <u>have</u> / <u>has</u>.

1. **A:** Tell me about your family.
   B: ......*I have*......... five sisters and one brother.

2. **A:** Tell me about your brother's family.
   B: .... a wife and one daughter.

3. **A:** Tell me about your daughter's family.
   B: .... a husband and three children, all boys.

4. **A:** You and your husband have no children?
   B: That's right. .... no children.

5. **A:** Tell me about your parents.
   B: .... seven children and fifteen grandchildren.

6. **A:** Tell me about Linda's family.
   B: .... a son and two daughters.

7. **A:** .... nine children.
   B: Wow! You have nine children? That's a busy house.

2 Look at the picture. Write sentences with <u>have</u> or <u>has</u>.

1. Michael: ......*He has a brother and a sister.*......
2. Rose: ....
3. Barbara and Martin: ....
4. Julia: ....
5. Louis: ....
6. Dan: ....

3 Match the numerals on the left with the written form of the numbers on the right. Draw a line.

1. 21   a forty
2. 34   b fifty-seven
3. 40   c one hundred
4. 45   d ninety-three
5. 57   e sixty-two
6. 62   f seventy-five
7. 75   g twenty-one
8. 88   h forty-five
9. 93   i eighty-eight
10. 100   j thirty-four

4 Write the next number in words.

1 ninety-nine, ninety-eight, ..., ninety-six, ninety-five
2 three, six, twelve, ..., forty-eight
3 twenty, twenty-five, thirty, thirty-five, ...
4 thirty-one, thirty-eight, forty-five, ...
5 sixty-one, sixty-three, sixty-five, ...
6 seventy, sixty, ..., forty, thirty

5 Complete each sentence with <u>have</u> or <u>has</u>. Then circle the letter of the correct response.

1 Abigail .... two brothers.
  a How old is he?   b How old are they?

2 I .... a new baby girl.
  a What's her name?   b What's his name?

3 They .... very old parents.
  a How old are they?   b How old is she?

4 He .... a young son.
  a How old is she?   b How old is he?

5 I .... three cousins.
  a What's their names?   b What are their names?

6 I .... a grandmother named Dutchie.
  a What's her name?   b How old is she?

6 Complete the conversations with sentences from the box. Three sentences are not used.

I'm tall.   I'm twenty-three.   Nineteen.   She's twelve.   She's very cute.
Well, I have one brother.   Well, I have one sister and one brother.

A: So, tell me about your family.
B: (1) ....
A: Really? How old is your sister?
B: (2) ....
A: And your brother?
B: (3) ....
A: And what about you?
B: (4) ....
A: Me, too! We're the same age!

34   UNIT 4

LESSON 3

1 Look at the picture. Then read the sentences. Check True or False.

	True	False
1 The man's hair is long.	☐	☐
2 The woman's hair is curly.	☐	☐
3 The man has a mustache.	☐	☐
4 The man is bald.	☐	☐
5 The woman has dark hair.	☐	☐
6 The woman has short, straight hair.	☐	☐

2 Look at each picture. Circle the correct words to complete each sentence.

1 His hair is (curly and blonde / straight and gray / curly and brown).

2 Her hair is (long and red / short and blonde / short and black).

3 Her hair is (long, wavy, and red / long, straight, and brown / short, curly, and red).

4 He (is bald with a beard / has short hair and no beard / is bald and doesn't have a beard).

3 Complete the sentences. Circle the correct verb.

1 You (are / have) a very pretty smile.
2 I love your hair. It (is / are) so curly.
3 My grandparents (are / have) really old.
4 Her uncle (is / has) a long beard.
5 Joe's hair (is / have) long and straight.
6 My mom (has / have) pretty, white hair.
7 You (is / have) such beautiful eyes.
8 He (is / has) bald like his father.

UNIT 4

4 Describe yourself and the people you know. Write sentences with <u>be</u> or <u>have</u>.

1 (a stranger) .... *His hair is curly and black. He has brown eyes* ....
2 (yourself) ....
3 (a friend) ....
4 (a family member) ....
5 (a classmate) ....

5 Complete the guessing game conversation with words from the box.

| beautiful smile | Guess who | I know | Is she short | long, brown, and wavy | My turn | Sorry | Who is it |

A: (1) .... ?
B: OK. (2) .... ?
A: Well, her hair is (3) .... and she has a (4) ....
B: (5) .... ?
A: No, she's tall.
B: (6) .... ! It's Melanie.
A: (7) .... That's wrong. It's Beth. (8) .... again.

LESSON 4

1 Read the article about three famous families. What information do you learn about them? Circle all the correct answers.

a their occupations
b their family relationships
c how they get to work
d places in their neighborhood

Famous Families

Penélope Cruz is a beautiful actor from Spain. Her younger sister Mónica is a famous actor, too. Her younger brother Eduardo is a singer. Penélope's husband is Spanish actor Javier Bardem. They have a son, Leo Encinas, and a daughter, Luna Encinas.

Timothy Carlton is an old British actor. His real name is Timothy Carlton Congdon Cumberbatch. His wife's name is Wanda Ventham. She is a British actor, too. They have a son and two grandsons. Their son is the famous British actor Benedict Cumberbatch. Benedict's wife is Sophie Hunter. She is a director and a writer. Benedict and Sophie have two young sons. Their names are Hal Auden Cumberbatch and Christopher Carlton Cumberbatch.

Ava Phillippe is a young actor from California. Ava's mother is Reese Witherspoon, a famous American actress. Her father is Ryan Phillippe. He is an actor, a director, and a TV producer. Ava's brother's name is Deacon Reese. He is a student.

2 Read about the famous families in Exercise 1 again. Then read the sentences and circle <u>True</u> or <u>False</u>.

1. Wanda Ventham is Sophie Hunter's mother. (True / False)
2. Christopher Carlton Cumberbatch is Hal Auden Cumberbatch's brother. (True / False)
3. Javier Bardem is Penélope Cruz's husband. (True / False)
4. Eduardo is Penélope Cruz's older brother. (True / False)
5. Penélope Cruz and Javier Bardem have a son. (True / False)
6. Ava Phillippe is Reese Witherspoon's daughter. (True / False)
7. Ava's father is an actor, director, and producer. (True / False)
8. Ava's brother, Deacon, is a famous musician. (True / False)
9. Timothy Carlton is Hal Auden Cumberbatch's grandfather. (True / False)
10. Deacon Reese is Ava Phillippe's student. (True / False)

VOCABULARY EXPANDER

Look at the picture. Write sentences about each of the people. Use a form of <u>be</u> and the adverb <u>very</u> or <u>so</u>.

She's / She is very slim.

GUIDED WRITING

Describe a famous person. Write six sentences. Use the questions as a guide. Begin each new sentence with a capital letter. End with a period.

His name is Chris Evans. He's 39 years old. He's tall and . . .

Questions
What's her / his name?
How old is she / he?
Is she / he tall or short?
Is she / he old or young?
Is she / he good-looking? cute?
What's her / his occupation?

JUST FOR FUN

A riddle for you! Read the sentence. Then answer the question.

1 Brothers and sisters have I none but that man's father is my father's son. Who is "that man"?
....

2 A mother and father have four daughters. Each daughter has a brother. How many people are in the family? ....

UNIT 5 Time and Events

Warm-up

1 Match times. Draw a line.

1 It's noon.   a 12:00 A.M.
2 It's five o'clock.   b 12:00 P.M.
3 It's eleven thirty.   c 12:55
4 It's a quarter to eight.   d 9:15

5 It's five to one.   e 5:00
6 It's midnight.   f 4:15
7 It's a quarter after four.   g 7:45
8 It's nine fifteen.   h 11:30

2 Look at the pictures. Are the people <u>early</u>, <u>late</u>, or <u>on time</u>? Complete the sentences.

1 He's ………………………… .   2 They're ………………………… .   3 She's ………………………… .

3 Look at each time. Read and circle the correct answer.

1 The movie is at twenty past one. They're
   (late / on time / early).

2 His interview is at a quarter to two. He's
   (late / on time / early).

UNIT 5   39

LESSON 1

1 Look at each picture. Write the type of event from the box. Two events are not used.

a concert   a game   a meeting   a movie   a party   a play   a talk   an exhibit

1 ....

2 ....

3 ....

4 ....

5 ....

6 ....

2 Complete the sentences with an event from Exercise 1.

1 Dr. Lee's .... will be on the importance of financial stability.
2 The art .... runs from Friday through Sunday.
3 The classical music .... is on Wednesday at Cameron Hall.
4 The .... starts when the DJ gets there.

3 Choose the correct words to complete the questions. Circle the letter.

1 .... time's the play?
   a When's   b When   c What

2 .... the concert?
   a When's   b When   c Where

3 The Spring Dance starts .... seven thirty.
   a at   b on   c from

4 .... their anniversary party?
   a What   b Where's   c When

40 UNIT 5

4 Complete the conversations. Use contractions when possible.

1 **A:** What .... are we meeting at the theater?
 B: .... a quarter after four.

2 **A:** .... the pre-screening of the movie?
 B: .... at seven o'clock.

3 **A:** .... time's the party?
 B: Get there .... 10 P.M.

4 **A:** .... your appointment?
 B: I need to be there .... 10:15.

5 Complete the conversation with words from the box. Two choices are not used.

| Eight thirty | late | No, we're not | OK | right on time | Seven thirty | Seven thirty | the game | Uh-oh |

A: Hey, Joe. What time's **(1)** .... ?
B: **(2)** ....
A: **(3)** .... , I forgot my jacket. Wait for me.
A: Are we **(4)** .... ?
B: **(5)** .... It's seven thirty now.
A: **(6)** .... ?
B: That's right. We're **(7)** ....

6 Look at the pictures. Then complete the conversation.

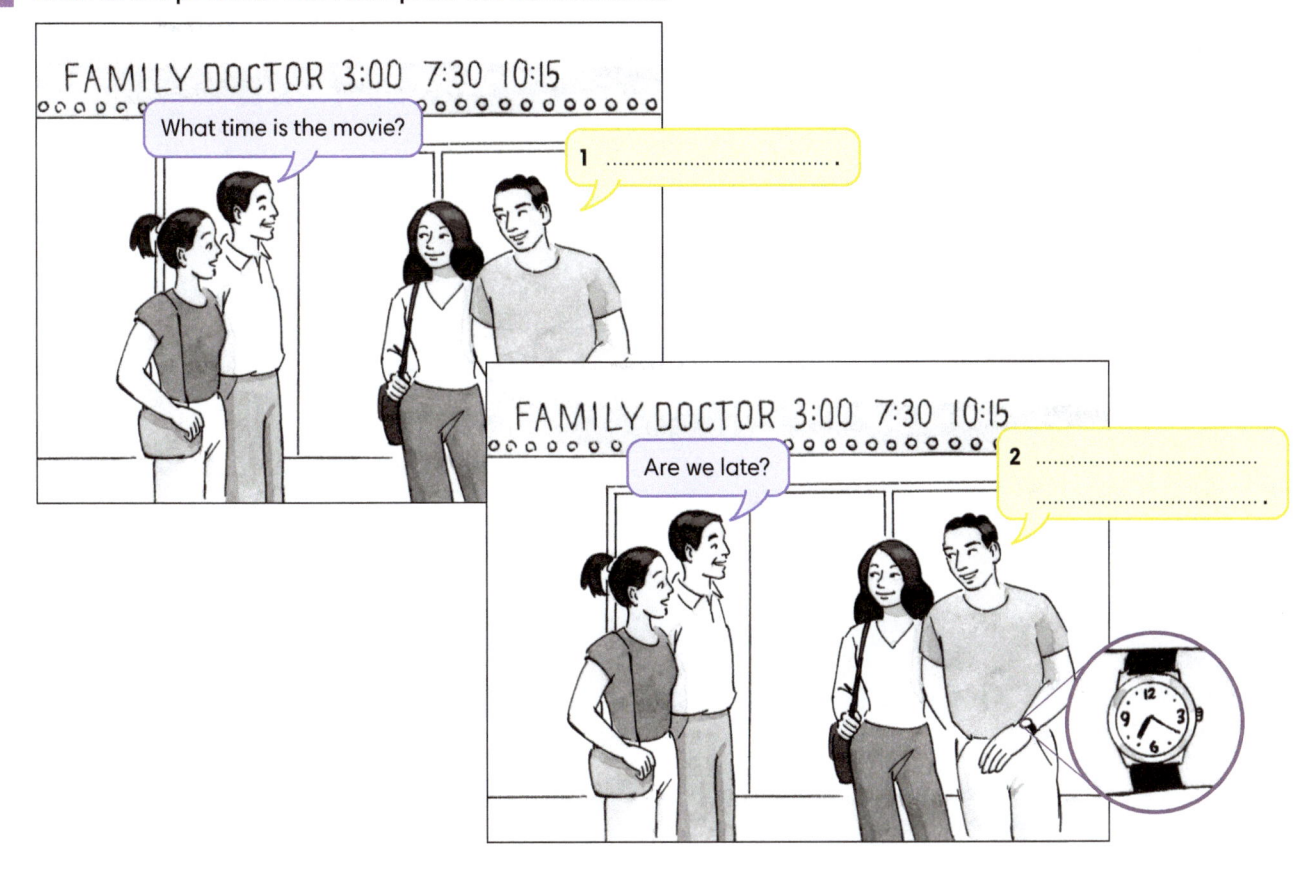

What time is the movie?

1 ....

Are we late?

2 ....
....

LESSON 2

1 Complete the calendar. Write in the days of the week in the correct order.

A WEEK

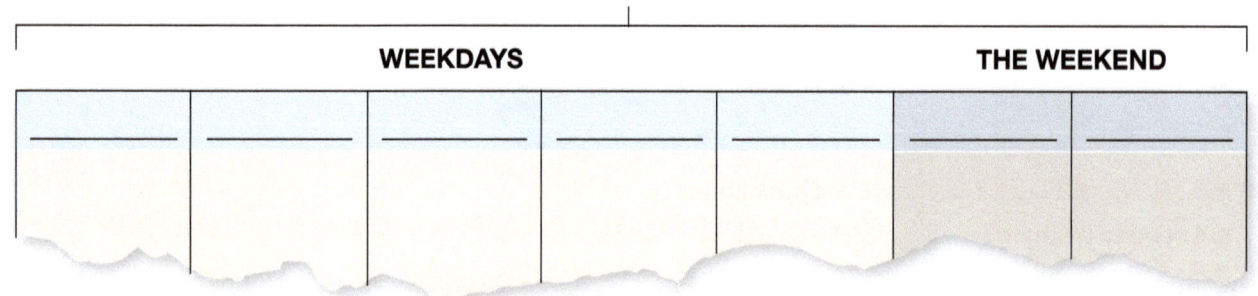

WEEKDAYS					THE WEEKEND	
_____	_____	_____	_____	_____	_____	_____

2 When is your English class? Circle the day or days on the calendar in Exercise 1. Write the times.

3 Circle the correct word or words to complete each conversation.

1 **A:** (What / When) day is Sarah's concert?
   B: It's on Saturday.
2 **A:** When's the new movie release?
   B: It's (on / at) Friday night.
3 **A:** (What day / When's) your photo exhibit?
   B: It starts at 7 P.M. on Sunday.
4 **A:** What time does the talk start?
   B: (On / At) four fifteen.
5 **A:** (When / What day) are we going to see the play?
   B: I think we should go on Thursday.
6 **A:** The art gallery is open Tuesday through Saturday.
   B: Let's go (on / at) Wednesday after class.
7 **A:** (What day / When's) the annual meeting this year?
   B: It's on the second Monday in March.
8 **A:** (When / What day) is best for us to meet this week?
   B: Probably Tuesday.
9 **A** What time's the office party?
   B: It's (at / in) noon.
10 **A:** (When's / What time) is the professor's talk?
   B: It begins (in / at) 8:30 A.M.

4 Look at the posters. Then read the sentences and check True, False, or No Information.

	True	False	No Information
1 The dinner is on Friday.	☐	☐	☐
2 The Winter Dance is in December.	☐	☐	☐
3 The game is at one o'clock.	☐	☐	☐
4 The concert is on Sunday.	☐	☐	☐
5 The movie is at 3:40 on Monday.	☐	☐	☐

5 Look at the posters in Exercise 4 again. Complete the questions and answers.

1 **A:** ....? **B:** It's .... Saturday.
2 **A:** ....? **B:** It's .... a quarter to eight.
3 **A:** ....? **B:** It's .... Thursday .... half past six.
4 **A:** ....? **B:** It's .... a quarter after seven.

6 Complete the conversation. Use the times and days from the posters in Exercise 4.

1 **You:** Hi, ... How are you?
   Your friend: Fine, thanks. And you?
2 **You:** .... Look. there's a .... on ....
   Your friend: Great! What time?
3 **You:** ....
   Your friend: OK. Let's meet at ....

UNIT 5

LESSON 3

1 Match the ordinal numbers with the people. Draw a line.

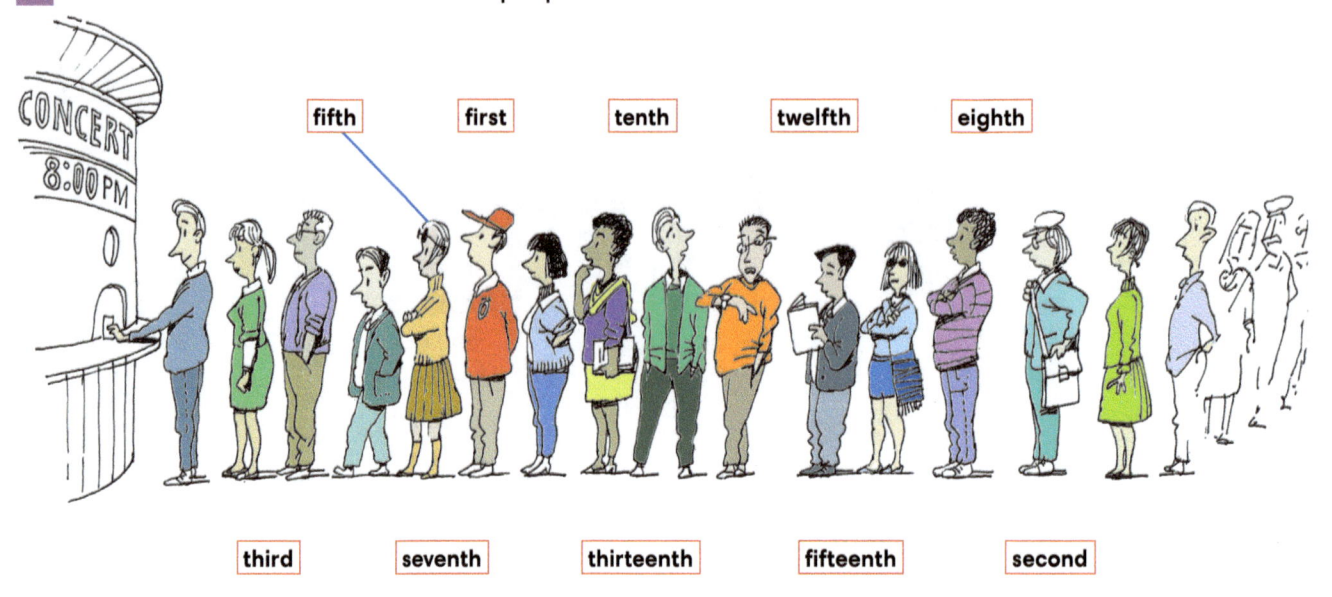

fifth   first   tenth   twelfth   eighth

third   seventh   thirteenth   fifteenth   second

2 Look at the pictures. Write the months for each type of weather where you live.

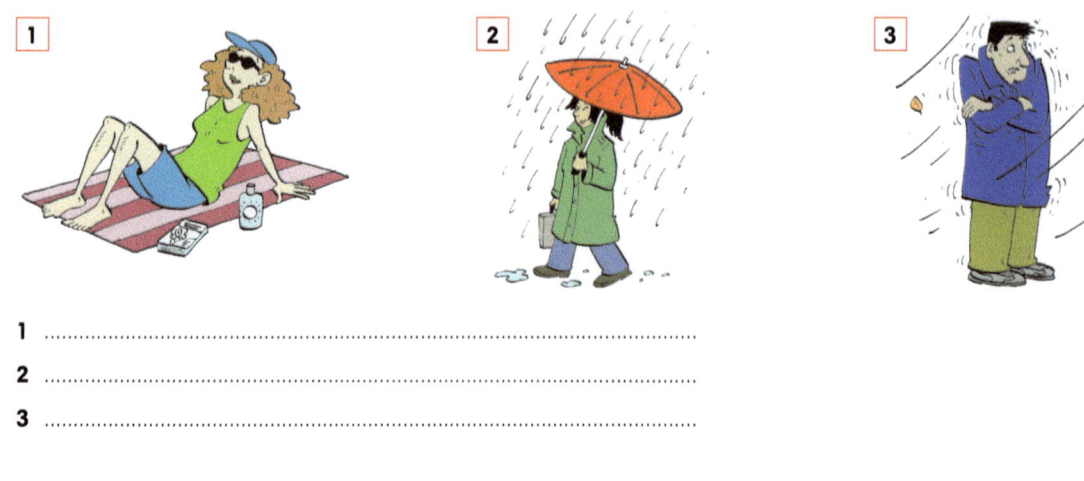

1
2
3

1 ....
2 ....
3 ....

3 Complete the sentences with an ordinal number or a month.

1 December is the .... month of the year.
2 .... is the first month of the year.
3 May is the .... month of the year.
4 .... is the eleventh month of the year.
5 .... is the seventh month of the year.
6 October is the .... month of the year.
7 .... is the third month of the year.
8 February is the .... month of the year.

4 Circle the correct words to complete the conversations.

1. **A:** (When's / What's / What month) is Malia's talk?
   B: It's in April.

2. **A:** Is the game at 8:00 tonight?
   B: No, it's (on / at / in) 7:30.

3. **A:** (When's / What's / What month) your next business trip?
   B: In September.

4. **A:** (When's / What's / What month) the date for the exhibit?
   B: June 1st.

5. **A:** When is the moonlight concert?
   B: It's (on / on the / in) 30th.

6. **A:** When's the next English class?
   B: (On / at / In) February.

5 Complete the conversations. Use <u>on</u>, <u>at</u>, <u>in</u>, and <u>the</u>.

1. **A:** When is your birthday?
   B: It's this month, ...*on the*... tenth.

2. **A:** When's the next movie?
   B: It's .... eight o'clock.

3. **A:** What month is your birthday?
   B: It's .... August.

4. **A:** Is the tennis match in the afternoon?
   B: No, it's .... the morning.

5. **A:** When's the new TV series start?
   B: Tonight .... 7:30.

6. **A:** When are we going out for dinner?
   B: .... Friday.

7. **A:** When is your appointment?
   B: It's .... 15th at 9:00 A.M.

DID YOU KNOW . . . ?

Q: How many people would you need to ask to find two people who share the same birthday?

A: According to the rules of probability, if you ask a random group of just 23 people there is a 50–50 chance that two of them will have the same birthday.

6 Complete the conversation with sentences from the box.

| Can I ask you a question? | My birthday's in April. | On November 7th. | Sure. | When's your birthday? |

A: (1) ....
B: (2) ....
A: (3) ....
B: (4) .... When's your birthday?
A: (5) .... On the 2nd.

UNIT 5

LESSON 4

1 Read the invitation and the neighborhood news. What information can you find? Circle all the correct answers.

a the date of a birthday party
b a time of a town meeting
c a location of a concert
d the subject of a talk
e the address of an art exhibit

Happy Birthday Tina!
It's a party for Tina's 20th birthday!

Date: Friday, June 11th
Time: From 7:00 to 9:00 P.M.
Place: Ricky's Restaurant
22 Fourth Street
Third Floor

NEIGHBORHOOD NEWS
JUNE 6TH TO JUNE 13TH

Midtown Market
110 Main St. (right across from the bus stop)
New Hours!
Weekdays: From 8 A.M. to 10 P.M.
Weekends: From 10 A.M. to 6 P.M.

Neighborhood Bank
Open June 6th—It's our first day!
15 First Avenue
Hours
Weekdays: From 9:00 A.M. to 4:00 P.M.
Wednesdays: From 9:00 A.M. to 7:00 P.M.
Saturdays and Sundays: Closed
"We speak Spanish, too!"

Talk for children and adults
Dr. Marcia Duran
"Don't be late! Be on time or early!"
June 10th from 6:30 to 8:00 P.M.
Davis High School
Meet Dr. Duran after the talk.

Student Art Exhibit: Young Artists
Saturday, June 16th
From 11:00 A.M. to 3:00 P.M.
City Art Gallery
17 Eighth Avenue
Sixth Floor

2 Read the invitation and the events page from Exercise 1 again. Match the phrases to make correct sentences. Draw a line.

1 Tina's party is on
2 The Midtown Market
3 On Wednesdays, the bank
4 June 6th is
5 The talk by Dr. Marcia Duran
6 The art exhibit opens at
7 The bus stop is
8 The City Art Gallery

a is open from 9 A.M. to 7 P.M.
b is on June 10th.
c right across from Midtown Market.
d is at 17 Eighth Avenue.
e Friday, June 11th.
f 11:00 A.M.
g opens at 8 A.M. on weekdays.
h the Neighborhood Bank's first day.

46 UNIT 5

VOCABULARY EXPANDER

Look at the pictures. Write the event.

1 a .... game

2 a ....

3 a .... match

4 a .... game

GUIDED WRITING

Write three sentences about your next English class. Include information about the day and date, time span, and location. Start with <u>There is</u>. Begin each new sentence with a capital letter. End with a period.

> There is an English class at Pagoda Academy. It's on Friday, November 3rd from 7:00 to 8:45. The school is on the corner of . . .

UNIT 5

UNIT 6 Clothes

Warm-up

1 Look at the clothes. Match the colors and the clothes. Draw a line.

1 a blue
2 a gray
3 a green
4 black and white
5 a purple
6 a red
7 an orange
8 a yellow

a shoes
b dress
c shirt
d tie
e skirt
f sweater
g blouse
h jacket

DID YOU KNOW . . . ?
- babies develop color vision at around two weeks old.
- the first color a baby sees is red.
- babies can see the full range of colors at about age five months.

LESSON 1

1 Look at the pictures. Circle the correct verb to complete the sentences.

1 Mr. West really (wants / has / needs) a jacket.

2 They (like / need / have) a taxi.

3 Mr. and Mrs. Berrier (like / have / want) a daughter.

4 Jill (wants / has / needs) a red moped.

5 Jackson really (likes / needs / has) that yellow tie.

6 Ms. Jones (has / needs / wants) that blue car.

2 Complete each sentence with the correct verb from the box.

| has | have | like | likes | need | needs | want | wants |

1 Your sweater is so pretty. I really .... it.
2 Jana and Jena both .... on red dresses today.
3 Karl .... a new suit for the office. The one in his closet doesn't fit.
4 I don't have anything to read this weekend. I .... a good book.
5 My brother .... a new computer. But his old one works fine.
6 Our neighbor .... the cutest puppy. Her name is Lulu.
7 I have so many shoes. I don't need them, but I .... some new boots.
8 Bart has to wear nice clothes for work. He .... to wear jeans on his days off.

UNIT 6 49

3 **Circle the correct form of the verbs to complete the sentences.**

1 All of my pants are old and worn out. I (**need** / needs / like / likes) to buy some new pants.
2 Tonya's favorite color is green. She (have / has / want / **wants**) the green blouse she saw online.
3 Joe collects funny ties. He (like / **likes** / have / has) to wear them to make people smile.
4 Rita (have / **has** / need / needs) a beautiful leather jacket. It's a rich brown color.
5 Our boys always (like / likes / want / **wants**) the latest style in athletic shoes.
6 We (**have** / has / like / likes) too many clothes in our closet. We need to clean it out.

4 **Look at the pictures. Write this, that, these, or those.**

1 .... shoes
2 .... tie 
3 .... skirt 
4 .... suits 
5 .... shoes 
6 .... jacket 

5 **Look at each picture. Write this, that, these or those and the clothes.**

1 ....*these shirts*........
2 .... 
3 .... 

50 UNIT 6

6 Complete the conversation with sentences from the box.

| I really like that shirt. | Really? | Thanks! | Yes. And I like those pants, too. | You're welcome. |

A: (1) ....
B: (2) ....
A: (3) ....
B: (4) ....
A: (5) ....

7 Look at the picture. Compliment each person on his or her clothes.

1 ....
....
....

2 ....
....
....

LESSON 2

1 Circle the correct words to complete the conversations.

1 **A:** I'm sorry, we (doesn't / don't / aren't) have this skirt in white.
   B: (Do / Does / Are) you have it in gray?

2 **A:** (Do / Does / Has) your son need a sports coat?
   B: Yes, he (do / have / does). He needs one for the school dance.

3 **A:** I (don't want / don't have / aren't) that tie in purple. I need it in blue.
   B: I'm sorry. We (doesn't have / don't have / no have) that tie in blue.

4 **A:** Does Cynthia (has / needs / need) a sweater for her dog?
   B: I don't think she needs one, but she would (like / want / do) one.

5 **A:** (Does / Do / Have) you like my new red shoes?
   B: Yes, (I have / I am / I do). Those shoes are so pretty.

6 **A:** (Does / Do / Are) that pink sweater come in an extra large?
   B: No, it (don't / doesn't / isn't), but why don't you try the large?

7 **A:** Sorry, but we (don't / doesn't / aren't) have this red sweater in medium.
   B: Too bad. (Are / Do / Does) you have that blue sweater in medium?

8 **A:** Unfortunately, I do (am not / don't / not) have that shirt in a large. (Do / Does / Are) you interested in an extra large?
   B: No, thank you.

UNIT 6   51

2 Complete the questions and statements. Use do or does and the correct form of the verb in parentheses. Use contractions when possible.

1 **A:** .... _Does_ .... your son .... _need_ .... white shirts for school? (need)
   B: Yes, he .... _does_ ....
2 **A:** .... you .... these shorts? (like)
   B: Yes, I .... But I .... them in a medium. (need)
3 **A:** I'm sorry, but we .... those shoes in a size 10. (not have)
   B: Oh, that's too bad. I really .... them. (like)
4 **A:** .... they .... that dress in yellow? (have)
   B: Yes, I think they .... I really .... to get it. (want)
5 **A:** .... your friend .... this black jacket? (want)
   B: No, she .... She already .... one. (have)
6 **A:** We have that blouse in several colors. .... you .... one? (want)
   B: I think my sister .... to get a couple of them. (want)
7 **A:** It's raining out. .... you .... an umbrella? (need)
   B: No, thanks. I .... a raincoat with a hood. (have)
8 **A:** They .... this tie in a neutral color. I only see bright colors. (not have)
   B: My father .... some gray, black, and blue ties. Let's keep looking. (need)
9 **A:** Her skirt is very colorful. .... you .... it? (like)
   B: I .... It's very pretty and it looks comfortable.

3 Complete the conversation with words from the box.

| a new suit for an interview | Excuse me | Great | I'm sorry | suit in a size 8 | That's too bad | Yes, we do |

A: (1) .... ? Do you have this sweater in red?
B: Red? (2) ....
A: (3) .... ! And my daughter needs (4) .... Do you have this (5) .... ?
B: No, we don't. (6) ....
A: (7) ....

4 Look at the clothes. Write a question. Ask for the color or the size in parentheses. Then complete the short answer.

(large)   (brown)   (small)   (black)

1 .... _Do you have this jacket in a large_ .... ? No, ... _we don't_ ....
2 .... ? Yes, ...
3 .... ? Yes, ...
4 .... ? No, ...

LESSON 3

1 Look at each picture. Circle the correct adjective to describe the clothes.

1 (clean / **dirty**)

2 (long / **short**)

3 (new / **old**)

4 (cheap / **expensive**)

5 (**loose** / tight)

2 Read the conversations. Circle the answer that best completes each response.

1 **A:** Do you like this skirt?
   B: Yes, I do, but it's a little (cheap / clean / long / **loose**). Do you have anything tighter?

2 **A:** Do you like this shirt?
   B: It's OK, but the medium size is very (dirty / loose / **tight** / cheap). Do you have it in a large?

3 **A:** Do you like this dress?
   B: It's very nice, but it's a bit (**expensive** / long / short / loose). I don't have much money.

4 **A:** Do you like these pants?
   B: No, not really. They're too (tight / **short** / dirty / cheap). I want them to be longer.

5 **A:** Do you like this suit?
   B: I do, but it costs so much. Here, this (clean / long / expensive / **cheap**) one will work just as well.

6 **A:** Do you like this blouse?
   B: No, not really. It's much too (tight / **long** / loose / clean) on you. It shouldn't go all the way to your knees.

3 Read the sentences. Correct the mistake.

1 It's a cheap very blouse.   *It's a very cheap blouse*.
2 That is dress expensive.   That is an expensive dress.
3 My shorts dirty are very.   My shorts are very dirty.
4 His pants are too tights.   His pants are too tight.
5 Her skirt very shorts is.   Her skirt is very short.
6 Pat's are shoes new.   Pat's shoes are new.

4 Complete the conversations with What, What color, What size, Why, or Which.

1 A: *What color* does he want?
   B: Black.

2 A: .... shirt does your son wear?
   B: He wears a medium.

3 A: .... dress does she like?
   B: The orange one.

4 A: .... do they like those shoes?
   B: I don't know. I guess because they're different.

5 A: .... jacket do you need?
   B: I need a red one.

6 A: .... do you need for Friday?
   B: I need a little black dress.

5 Read about Sasha and Erika. Then complete the conversations. Write questions with Why, What, or Which.

Sasha and Erika are looking for new clothes. They're at StyleRight, a clothing store. They need clothes for work. Sasha is an accountant, and Erika is an artist. Sasha's suit is old, and she needs a new one. She also wants new shoes. Erika needs a black dress for an exhibit on Saturday.

StyleRight has a black suit, a brown suit, a gray suit, and a blue suit in Sasha's size. She likes the gray one. StyleRight has a short dress and a long dress in black. Erika wants the long dress. But the long dress is very expensive. StyleRight doesn't have shoes. Sasha says, "Look! There's a shoe store across the street."

1 A: *What are Sasha and Erika looking for* ?   B: New clothes.
2 A: .... ?   B: Because her suit is old.
3 A: .... ?   B: For an exhibit.
4 A: .... ?   B: The gray suit.
5 A: .... ?   B: The long dress.
6 A: .... ?   B: They don't have shoes.

54 UNIT 6

6 Look at the pictures. Complete the questions and the answers.

What do you think of *this dress*?

1 YOU ....
....

What do you think of ....?

2 YOU ....
....

What do you think of ....?

3 YOU ....
....

What do you think of ....?

4 YOU ....
....

LESSON 4

1 Look at the clothing store website. What information can you find? Circle all the correct answers.

a kinds of clothes   b colors   c prices   d sizes   e store locations

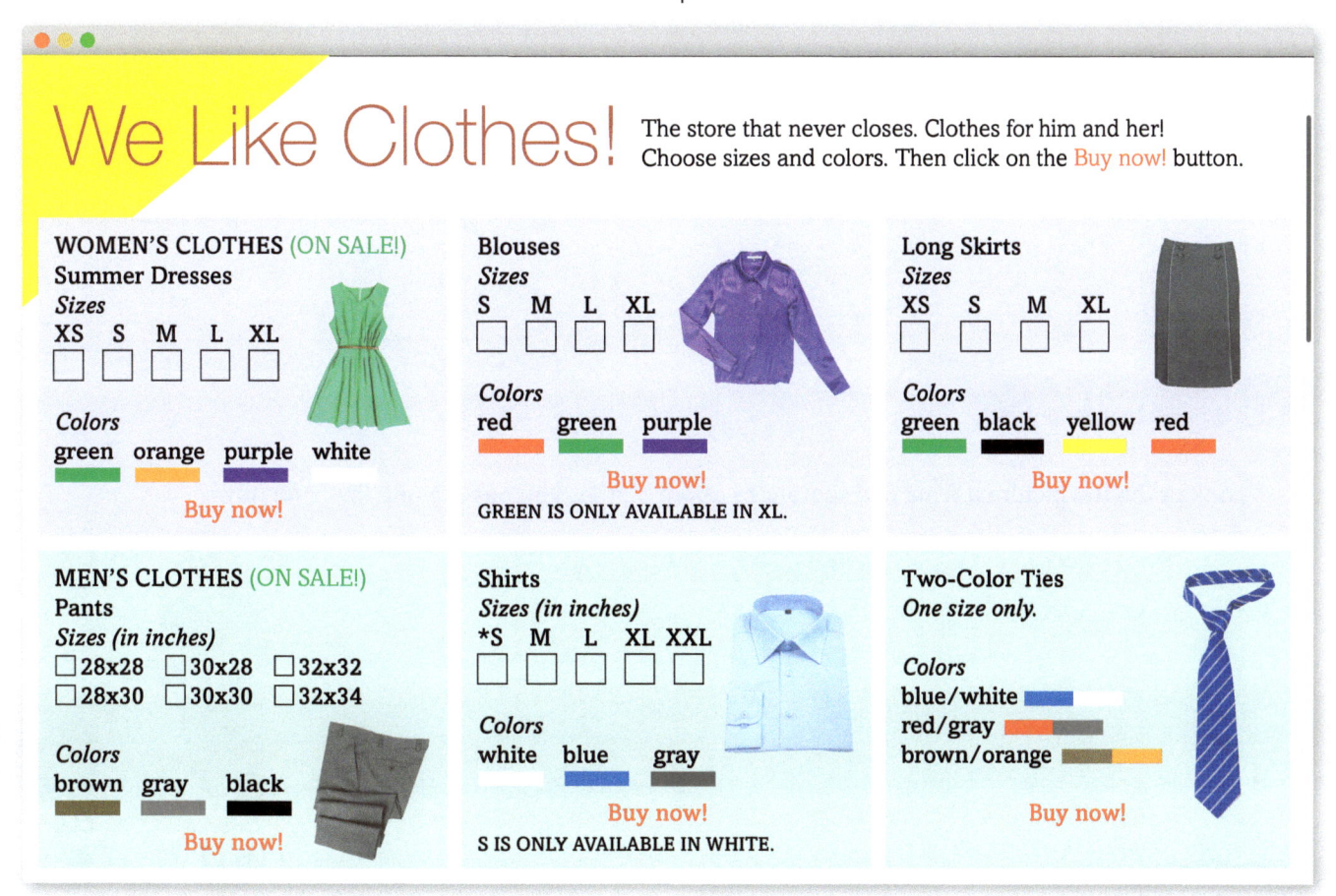

We Like Clothes!

The store that never closes. Clothes for him and her! Choose sizes and colors. Then click on the Buy now! button.

WOMEN'S CLOTHES (ON SALE!)
Summer Dresses
Sizes
XS S M L XL
☐ ☐ ☐ ☐ ☐

Colors
green orange purple white

Buy now!

Blouses
Sizes
S M L XL
☐ ☐ ☐ ☐

Colors
red green purple

Buy now!
GREEN IS ONLY AVAILABLE IN XL.

Long Skirts
Sizes
XS S M XL
☐ ☐ ☐ ☐

Colors
green black yellow red

Buy now!

MEN'S CLOTHES (ON SALE!)
Pants
Sizes (in inches)
☐ 28x28 ☐ 30x28 ☐ 32x32
☐ 28x30 ☐ 30x30 ☐ 32x34

Colors
brown gray black

Buy now!

Shirts
Sizes (in inches)
*S M L XL XXL
☐ ☐ ☐ ☐ ☐

Colors
white blue gray

Buy now!
S IS ONLY AVAILABLE IN WHITE.

Two-Color Ties
One size only.

Colors
blue/white
red/gray
brown/orange

Buy now!

UNIT 6   55

2 Review the webpage from Exercise 1 again. Then read the sentences. Check <u>True</u> or <u>False</u>.

	True	False
1 The clothes store has mens' pants in gray.	☐	☐
2 They have purple dresses in size XS.	☐	☐
3 A white and red tie is available.	☐	☐
4 Long skirts are available in size L.	☐	☐
5 Green blouses are available in size XL.	☐	☐
6 The website has gray shirts in size S.	☐	☐
7 The website has size 32x32 pants in black.	☐	☐
8 Ties are available in multiple sizes.	☐	☐

VOCABULARY EXPANDER

Look at the pictures. Write the missing letters to spell the clothes or shoes.

1 s _ d _ _ s
2 n i _ t _ w _
3 _ o _ s
4 j _ _ _ s

GUIDED WRITING

Look at the the pictures. Write five sentences about clothes you need, want, like, and have.

I need a suit like Charlie's. But I really like to wear jeans like Claire's. . . .

Charlie   Claire

56   UNIT 6

UNIT 7 Free Time and Chores

Warm-up

1 Look at the pictures. Write the activities people do at home.

1 get ....
2 .... my teeth 
3 get .... 
4 .... breakfast 
5 come .... 
6 .... dinner 
7 .... 
8 .... undressed 
9 .... to .... 

2 Put your own morning activities in order. Write ordinal numbers (1st, 2nd, . . .) on the lines. Write an X next to the activities you don't do.

.... take a shower / bath
.... eat breakfast
.... put on makeup
.... get up

.... shave
.... get dressed
.... brush my teeth
.... comb / brush my hair

UNIT 7   57

3 Look at the pictures and information. Match the phrases to make sentences about the people and their activities. Draw a line.

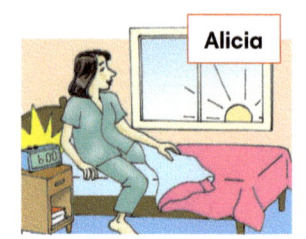

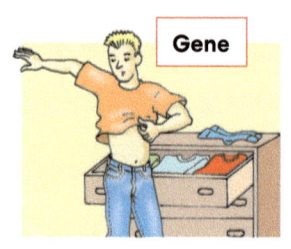

1 Alicia
2 Frank and Gina
3 Miriam
4 Gene
5 Jacob
6 Maya and Sue

a gets dressed at 7:00 A.M.
b makes dinner at 6:00 P.M.
c brush their teeth at 8:00 A.M.
d watches TV at 7:30 P.M.
e gets up at 6:00 A.M.
f take a shower and a bath at 8:00 P.M.

LESSON 1

1 Look at the pictures. Write the household chores.

1 ....
2 ....
3 ....
4 ....

2 Read about Lara's family. Which household chores do they each do? Circle the correct answer.

1 Lara's mother (washes the dishes / takes out the garbage / cleans the house).

2 Her mother and father (go shopping / clean the house / do the laundry).

3 Lara and her brother (clean the house / do the laundry / wash the dishes).

4 Her grandfather (takes a nap / cleans the house / does the laundry).

My name is Lara. On a typical Saturday, my family and I do household chores. My father gets up early and washes the dishes. Then he and my mother go shopping. My brother Joel and I clean the house. My grandfather does the laundry, and my grandmother . . . well, the garbage is her job, but she never does it! My mother takes out the garbage after lunch, and my grandmother takes a nap!

58 UNIT 7

3 Circle the correct form of the verb to complete each sentence.

1 My brother (get / **gets**) dressed before breakfast.
2 We (**brush** / brushes) our teeth after breakfast.
3 Elaine (put on / **puts on**) makeup before leaving for work.
4 Wayne (**comes** / come) home at 5:30 P.M.
5 Joel and Allison (makes / **make**) dinner at 6:00 P.M.
6 Karl (**watches** / watch) TV before bed.
7 Shelby (go / **goes**) to bed at midnight.

4 Look at the pictures. Write sentences about the chores Mr. and Mrs. Rand do. First, write a question with <u>Who</u> for each picture. Then answer the questions.

1 Who washes the dishes ?
  Mr. Rand washes the dishes .

2 .... ?
  ....

3 .... ?
  ....

4 .... ?
  ....

5 .... ?
  ....

5 Complete the conversation with words from the box. Two words are not used.

| dinner | does the dishes | I do | my husband's | Oh |
| So | That depends | the garbage | the laundry | |

A: **(1)** .... , who does **(2)** .... in your house?

B: Actually, **(3)** ....

A: And who takes out the garbage?

B: **(4)** .... on how busy we are. We usually take turns.

A: And who **(5)** .... ?

B: Oh, that's **(6)** .... job. But I make **(7)** .... most nights.

DID YOU KNOW . . . ?
A survey of 30 countries showed that women, on average, do 4 hours and 22 minutes of chores a day. Men spend just 2 hours and 16 minutes doing chores.

UNIT 7   59

LESSON 2

1 Look at each picture. Circle the correct free-time activity.

1 (go out for dinner / visit friends / listen to music)

2 (go to the movies / take a walk / exercise)

3 (take a nap / read / visit friends)

4 (take a walk / go to the movies / go out for dinner)

5 (exercise / read / take a walk)

6 (visit friends / exercise / take a nap)

2 Complete each conversation. Circle the correct letter.

1 **A:** .... is the movie?
   B: It's at 6:00.
   a What day   b How often   c What time

2 **A:** .... do you listen to music?
   B: I listen to music all the time.
   a What time   b How often   c What day

3 **A:** How often do you .... dinner?
   B: Twice a week.
   a take a   b go to the   c go out for

4 **A:** When do you exercise at the gym?
   B: Usually .... a week.
   a three days   b on Fridays   c every

5 **A:** On what day does she take a nap?
   B: .... Sundays.
   a Every   b On   c Once a

6 **A:** How often do you text your friends.
   B: At least ten .... a day.
   a in   b twice   c times

60 UNIT 7

3 Look at Larry's weekly schedule. Then write questions with <u>How often</u> and complete the answers.

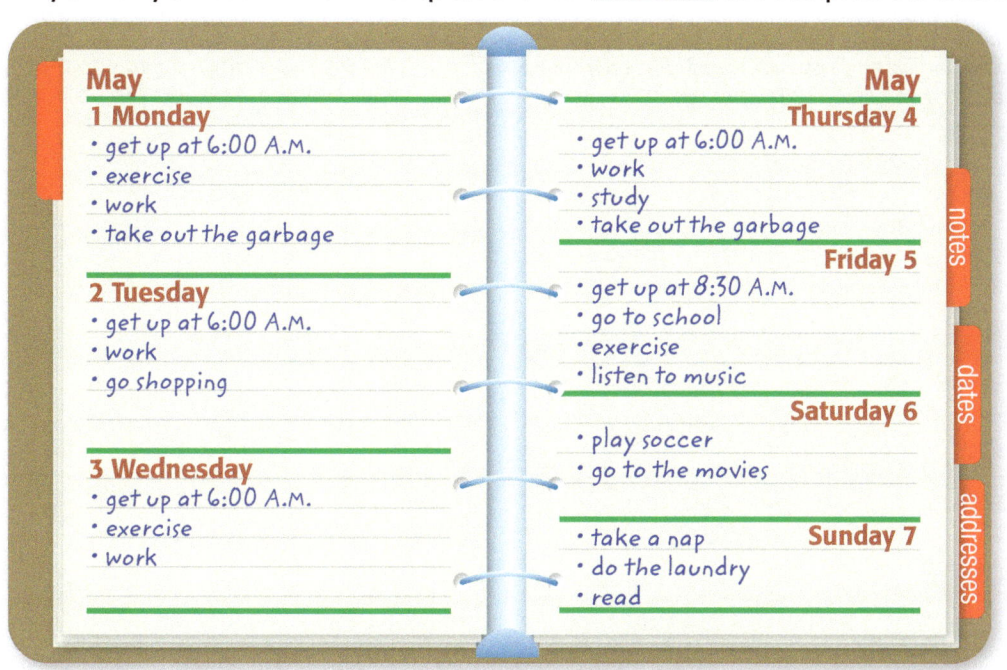

May
1 Monday
- get up at 6:00 A.M.
- exercise
- work
- take out the garbage

2 Tuesday
- get up at 6:00 A.M.
- work
- go shopping

3 Wednesday
- get up at 6:00 A.M.
- exercise
- work

May
Thursday 4
- get up at 6:00 A.M.
- work
- study
- take out the garbage

Friday 5
- get up at 8:30 A.M.
- go to school
- exercise
- listen to music

Saturday 6
- play soccer
- go to the movies

Sunday 7
- take a nap
- do the laundry
- read

1 **A:** *How often does Larry go to school* ?
   B: He .... once a week.

2 **A:** .... ?
   B: He .... twice a week.

3 **A:** .... ?
   B: He .... three times a week.

4 **A:** .... ?
   B: He .... four times a week.

4 Look at Larry's schedule in Exercise 3 again. Answer the questions.

1 When does Larry work?
   ....

2 When does he go to school?
   ....

3 What day does Larry play soccer?
   ....

4 What time does he get up on Fridays?
   ....

5 What days does Larry take out the garbage?
   ....

5 Complete the conversation using sentences from the box.

Actually, I take a lot of walks. I like nature. What about you?	Once or twice a week.
I mean, do you listen to music? Read? Go to the movies?	Really? How often do you do that?
Me? I go to the movies with my friends.	So, Brayden, what do you do in your free time?
My free time?	

A: (1) ....

B: (2) ....

A: (3) ....

B: (4) ....

A: (5) ....

B: (6) ....

A: (7) ....

LESSON 3

1 On a typical weekday, do you . . . ? Check <u>Always</u>, <u>Usually</u>, <u>Sometimes</u> or <u>Never</u>.

	Always	Usually	Sometimes	Never
1 eat breakfast	☐	☐	☐	☐
2 brush your teeth after breakfast	☐	☐	☐	☐
3 exercise in the morning	☐	☐	☐	☐
4 go out for lunch	☐	☐	☐	☐
5 watch TV in the evening	☐	☐	☐	☐
6 take a shower at night	☐	☐	☐	☐

On a typical weekend, do you . . . ? Check <u>Always</u>, <u>Usually</u>, <u>Sometimes</u> or <u>Never</u>.

	Always	Usually	Sometimes	Never
1 study	☐	☐	☐	☐
2 visit friends	☐	☐	☐	☐
3 go to the movies	☐	☐	☐	☐
4 take a walk	☐	☐	☐	☐
5 go out for dinner	☐	☐	☐	☐
6 take a nap	☐	☐	☐	☐

2 Look at your answers in Exercise 1. Write five sentences about your activities. Follow the model.

> On weekdays, I usually exercise in the morning.

3 Think about the leisure activities of some of your family members and friends. Complete the chart.

Name / Relationship	Activity	Time expression	Frequency
grandmother	take a nap	in the afternoon	usually

4 Complete the conversation with sentences from the box.

> But I'm free on Sunday.   Great idea!   I'm sorry. I usually clean house on Saturdays.   Perfect. See you then.

A: Hey, Fran. Let's go out to lunch sometime.

B: (1) ....

A: Are you busy this Saturday?

B: (2) ....

    (3) ....

A: OK! Sundays are good for me.

B: (4) ....

UNIT 7   63

LESSON 4

1 Read the interview. What do the people talk about? Circle the correct answer.

a chores   b free-time activities   c weekend plans

"At Home" with actor, Jenna Kirby

In this interview, we visit Jenna Kirby at her beautiful house and ask her about household chores.

AH: This is a beautiful home. And so clean! How often do you vacuum the floors?
Jenna: I never vacuum! A robot vacuums the floors. I love it!
AH: Awesome! Those big windows are very clean, too. When do you wash them?
Jenna: I never wash the windows.
AH: Really? Why are they so nice and clean?
Jenna: Because another robot cleans them on Saturdays.
AH: Oh! You use a robot for that, too? Wow! And how about for cooking? Does a robot make you lunch?
Jenna: Of course not! I don't have a robot cook! But, I want one because I don't have time! My daughter always makes breakfast for me. At work, a cook makes lunch for the actors. It's always very good. Actually, I often eat too much. Do you think this dress is tight on me?
AH: Oh, no! It's perfect. Your clothes are always gorgeous!
Jenna: Oh! Thank you!
AH: How often do you do laundry? Every day?
Jenna: Oh, no! I'm too busy! I go to work at the studio at 6:00 A.M. A makeup artist puts on my makeup from 6:00 to 6:30. Then it's work, work, work! When I have free time at work, I study my lines and I exercise. After work, I visit friends and go out for dinner. I come home very late. After I come home, I read or listen to music.
AH: So, who does your laundry?
Jenna: My husband does. He does it twice or three times a week. And he does a very good job!

2 Read the article from Exercise 1 again. Circle the correct words to complete the sentences.

1 Jenna Kirby doesn't do household (plans / **chores**).
2 (Jenna's daughter / **A robot**) vacuums the floors.
3 Jenna wants a robot that can (**cook** / do her makeup).
4 Jenna's daughter makes her (lunch / **breakfast**) every day.
5 (Jenna / **Someone else**) puts on her makeup in the morning.
6 Jenna (**often** / never) eats too much for lunch.
7 During free time, Jenna studies her lines and (takes a nap / **exercises**).
8 Jenna eats dinner (at / **after**) work.
9 After work she sometimes (**visits friends** / goes to the movies).
10 Jenna's husband does the laundry (every day / **two or three times a week**).

VOCABULARY EXPANDER

1 Look at the pictures. Complete the words for the household chores. Write the missing letters.

1 _ u _ _   2 v _ c _ _ m   3 m _ _   4 s _ _ e _

2 Look at Mark and Connie's schedule. Write four sentences about their chores. Use the simple present tense and frequency adverbs or time expressions.

Sunday	Monday	Tuesday	Wednesday	Thursday	Friday	Saturday
Mark sweeps	Mark vacuums Mark sweeps	Mark sweeps	Mark vacuums Mark sweeps	Mark sweeps	Mark vacuums Mark sweeps	Mark sweeps
Connie dusts		Connie mops				Connie mops

....
....
....
....

GUIDED WRITING

Interview a friend. Ask about his or her typical week. Use the questions as a guide. Write six sentences. Use frequency adverbs <u>always</u>, <u>usually</u>, <u>sometimes</u>, and <u>never</u> and time expressions.

On weekday mornings, Jake usually gets up late, at 10:00.
He never . . .

Questions
What do you do in the morning?
What do you do in the afternoon?
What do you do in the evening?
What do you do on the weekend?
How often do you go to the movies?
How often do you exercise?

UNIT 7

UNIT 8 Houses and Homes

Warm-up

1 Complete the chart. Write the furniture and appliances from the box in the correct room. Two choices are used more than once.

| a bathtub | a bed | a bookcase | a dresser | a lamp | a microwave | a mirror |
| a refrigerator | a shower | a sink | a sofa | a stove | a toilet | a TV |

A Living Room	A Kitchen	A Bedroom	A Bathroom
a bookcase	a stove	a bed	a mirror

2 Look at the rooms. Write the furniture and appliances you see.

1 a living room
A ....
B ....
C ....

2 a bedroom
A ....
B ....
C ....

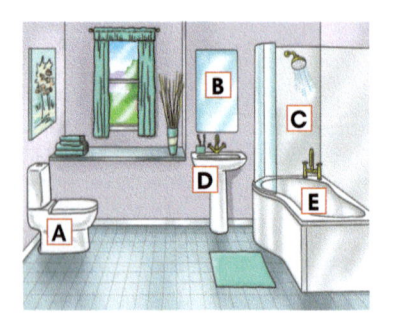

3 a bathroom
A ....
B ....
C ....
D ....
E ....

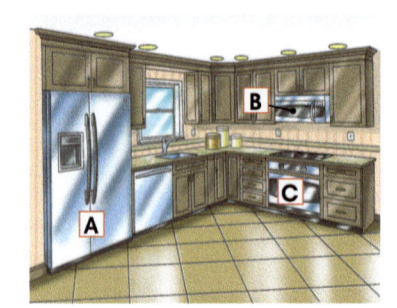

4 a kitchen
A ....
B ....
C ....

3 Look at the pictures. Write in the correct words to identify the building or room. Use the words from the box.

| apartment | apartment building | a house | an office building | office |

1 ....
2 ....
3 ....
4 ....
5 ....

4 Use the words from the box in Exercise 3 to complete the paragraph.

Nina: I'm an editor, and I work from home. I live and work in **(1)** .... with my husband and two dogs. It's a good-sized home with a huge backyard. I like it.

Peter: I'm a sales manager, and I work in **(2)** .... on Simms Street. It's not a very tall building, but I have a very large **(3)** .... with a window that looks out on a park.

Cybil: I'm a college student. I recently moved into my own **(4)** ...., and I love it. So far, I've met about five other people who live in my **(5)** .... They seem really nice.

LESSON 1

1 Look at the pictures. Write the parts of the buildings. Use the words from the box.

| a balcony | a door | a garage | a window | an elevator | downstairs |
| stairs | the first floor | the second floor | the third floor | upstairs |

1 ....
2 ....
3 ....
4 ....
5 ....
6 ....
7 ....
8 ....
9 ....
10 ....
11 ....

UNIT 8   67

2 Circle the correct words to complete the paragraphs.

Tim: I like my house. It's a large, two-story brick building with a very tall **(1)** (gate / door / balcony) that opens into a long hallway. The living room is off to the right, and the **(2)** (stairs / windows / elevator) with wood railings are on the left. The kitchen and dining room are farther back on the first floor. There's also a **(3)** (upstairs / stairs / downstairs) bathroom. Upstairs, on the **(4)** (third floor / balcony / second floor) there are four bedrooms and a game room. My family loves this house.

Pamela: Because I live in the middle of downtown, I have a small apartment with one bedroom and one bathroom. The kitchen is a really nice size though. And since my apartment is on the **(5)** (fourth floor / balcony / upstairs), I have a nice view out my living room window. My favorite part of my apartment is the **(6)** (stairs / windows / balcony). I love to sit out there and watch the people moving about below. Recently, I met another lady in the same building. She's just below me on the **(7)** (elevator / third floor / downstairs). Her apartment is so close, I usually take the **(8)** (stairs / window / second floor) when I visit her.

3 Complete each sentence. Circle the correct words.

1 How many floors .... in your apartment building?
   a are there   b there are   c you have

2 .... three large windows in their dining room.
   a There is   b They are   c There are

3 .... a garage at this house?
   a Is there   b Are there   c There is

4 I'm sorry, but .... a third-floor apartment available.
   a there isn't   b there aren't   c there's no

5 .... a bathroom upstairs and one downstairs.
   a There are   b There's   c Is there

4 Look at the floor plans for two apartments. What are they like? Write sentences with <u>There's</u> and <u>There are</u>.

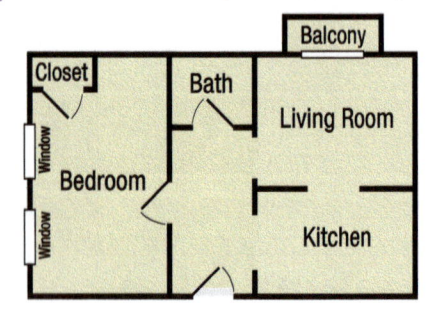

1 *There's one large bedroom* .
2 ....
3 ....
4 ....

5 *There are three bedrooms* .
6 ....
7 ....
8 ....

5 Write four questions about your home. Use <u>Is there</u>, <u>Are there</u>, or <u>How many</u>. Then answer the questions.

1 ....? 3 ....?
....
2 ....? 4 ....?
....

6 Complete the conversation with sentences from the box. Two sentences are not used.

> Actually, no, I don't. I live in an apartment.   Actually, yes, I do.
> Do you live in a house or an apartment?   Does it have a garage?
> Is it on the second floor?   Is it small or large?
> Is there a balcony?   Well, it's kind of small.

A: Do you live in a house, Joseph?

B: **(1)** ....

A: What's it like?

B: **(2)** .... There's one bedroom, one bathroom, a small kitchen, and a living room area.

A: **(3)** ....

B: Yes, the balcony is the best part. What about you? **(4)** ....

A: I live in an apartment, too.

B: Really? **(5)** ....

A: It's pretty small, like yours.

B: Do you like it?

A: **(6)** ....

LESSON 2

1 Look at each picture. Write the furniture and appliances you see.

1 a home office

A ....
B ....
C ....
D ....

2 a dining room

A ....
B ....
C ....

UNIT 8

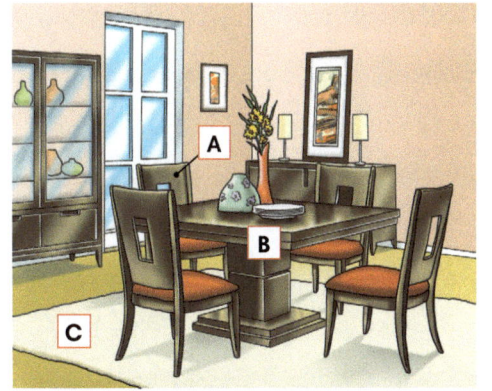

2 Complete the paragraphs. Circle the correct furniture.

Brenda: I like my job. I work for a bank, but I work from home. Every weekday, I log in to my **(1)** (computer / phone / lamp) and open up the files I need. My computer is set up on my **(2)** (chair / desk / rug) beside a plant and a picture of my family. There's also a **(3)** (table / chair / phone) on my desk. The **(4)** (printer / table / chair) that I sit in is very comfortable, which is a good thing, since I sit in it a lot.

Andrew: Because I live in a small apartment, I don't have the space for a home office. So, I work at the **(5)** (computer / lamp / table) in my dining room. I send completed documents to the **(6)** (phone / printer / computer) in my bedroom. I don't mind walking to the other room. It gives me a chance to get up and stretch. When I come back, I usually kick off my shoes. I like to work with my bare feet resting on the soft **(7)** (rug / lamp / chair) beneath the table.

3 Complete the conversation with sentences from the box.

| Actually, I think the chair is beautiful.   And what about this rug? I think it's pretty, too. |
| No offense, Karen, but I think it's really ugly.   No way!   This is a nice chair. What do you think? |

A: (1) ....
B: (2) ....
A: (3) ....
B: (4) ....
A: (5) ....

LESSON 3

1 Circle the correct word or words to complete each conversation.

1. **A:** Where (do / does) your brother live?
   B: He lives (at / on / in) 222 Merchant Trail.

2. **A:** Where (do / does) you work.
   B: I work (at / on / in) the pharmacy downtown.

3. **A:** Where (do / does) your children study?
   B: (At / On / In) the dining room, at the table.

4. **A:** (Where / When) do your parents live?
   B: They live (at / on / in) a house in Maryland.

5. **A:** Where (do / does) your daughter live?
   B: She lives (at / on / in) Sherman Street.

6. **A:** (Where / When) does Gabriel work?
   B: He works (at / on / in) the seventh floor at the bank.

2 Complete the conversations. Use prepositions of place and the verb <u>be</u> or the simple present tense.

1. **A:** .... she .... near you?
   B: No, she lives .... Saddle Creek Avenue.
2. **A:** .... do you .... ?
   B: I work .... the shoe factory.
3. **A:** Where .... you .... ?
   B: I live .... an apartment on South Street.
4. **A:** Is your apartment .... the first floor?
   B: No. I .... on the fifth floor.
5. **A:** .... your house have a garage?
   B: No, it doesn't. We park .... the driveway.

3 Look at the pictures. Write the places.

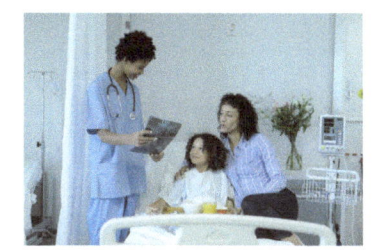

1 ....

2 ....

3 ....

4 ....

5 ....

6 ....

7 ....

8 ....

UNIT 8   71

4 Where does each person go? Match the sentences with the locations. Draw a line.

1 I enjoy shopping so much. I go here every Saturday.
2 My wife had to have a special surgery. I took her to the best place.
3 Janine loves football games. She goes here once a week.
4 Jeremy takes the train to and from work on weekdays. He goes here.
5 My children and I love to ride our bikes. Every Sunday we go here.
6 Rebecca loves paintings. She looks at pictures here twice a month.
7 We like to travel, especially by plane. You can find us here every other month.
8 Sam likes to take the bus when he is in a new city. He starts off here.

a a train station
b a museum
c an airport
d a mall
e a hospital
f a bus station
g a stadium
h a park

5 Complete the sentences in your own words.

I live . . .

in

on

at

next to

near

across the street from

6 Complete the conversation with words from the box. Two choices are not used.

Across the street from   around the corner   between   It's great   Near the mall   next to the   Sounds nice

A: Where do you live? Far from here?
B: No. I live on Indigo Road. **(1)** ....
A: What's the neighborhood like?
B: **(2)** .... ! The neighbors are really friendly. We often meet up at the playground. And **(3)** .... from us is a park with bike trails.
A: **(4)** ....
B: It is. And where do you live?
A: I live on Amarillo Street. **(5)** .... the school.

72 UNIT 8

LESSON 4

1 Read the descriptions of two people's homes. What information do you learn? Circle all the correct answers.

a number of rooms   b furniture and appliances   c places in the neighborhood   d type of building

Welcome to My Apartment!

This week, two of our readers describe their apartments. Is your taste in apartments more like John's or Maria's? Read and find out!

John Parker:

My apartment is small, but I like it that way—it's cheap! In the apartment, there are only three rooms: a living room, a small kitchen, and a bathroom. I don't have a wife or children, so I don't need a big apartment. I work at home, so the living room is also my office. There is a big chair and a small desk, a sofa, a bookcase, and a lamp. On sunny days, I don't need the lamp because there is a large window. The bathroom has a sink, a toilet, and a shower, but there is no bathtub. That's OK, though. I don't like baths. In the kitchen, there is a small refrigerator, a stove, a microwave, and a sink. I cook my meals every day—I think it's fun! The building doesn't have a garage, but that's no problem because I don't have a car. Also, I don't have a bed. At night, I sleep on the sofa. But there is one bad thing. My apartment is on the 4th floor, and the building doesn't have an elevator!

Maria Lopez:

I live in a large apartment with my husband, son, and daughter. We live on the 20th floor, but the elevator is very fast. The apartment has three bedrooms, a living room, three bathrooms with big bathtubs, an office, a kitchen, and a large balcony. It's expensive, but we love it. There are beautiful rugs in all the rooms. In the kitchen, there is a very big refrigerator because my children are young and they eat a lot! There is also a table with four chairs, and there are two sinks. We wash a lot of dishes. The living room has a large chair, a sofa, two small tables with lamps, but no TV. We don't watch TV. My husband goes to work every day—he's a teacher—but I work at home in the office. It has a big desk with a chair. The building has a big garage. That's great because we're a two-car family!

2 Reread the article from Exercise 1. What does each apartment have? Complete the chart with words from the box. Two choices are not used.

a balcony   a bookcase   a desk   a garage   a microwave
a refrigerator   a shower   a sofa   an elevator

John's Apartment	Maria's Apartment	Both Apartments

DID YOU KNOW . . . ?
A home in Mumbai, India is the world's largest, tallest, and most expensive single-family house. It covers 37,161 square meters and is 173 meters tall. It has 27 floors, 9 different elevators, and a garage that fits 168 cars. It cost $2 billion to build.

UNIT 8

VOCABULARY EXPANDER

1 Look at the pictures. Write the words for the home and office items.

1  .... 2  .... 3  .... 4 ....

5  .... 6  .... 7  .... 8 ....

2 Read the words. Circle the word that doesn't belong.

1 knife / napkin / fork / spoon
2 shower curtain / bath mat / medicine cabinet / fire escape
3 dishwasher / plate / bowl / saucer
4 coffee maker / fax machine / garden / filing cabinet
5 faucet / food processor / pot / frying pan
6 sheet / blanket / pillow / place mat

GUIDED WRITING

Write five sentences about your dream home. Use the questions as a guide.

My dream home is an apartment in Paris. It has ...

Questions
Is it a house or an apartment?
Where is it?
How many bedrooms are there?
How many bathrooms are there?
Is the kitchen small or large?
Is there a living room?
Is there a home office?

UNIT 9 Activities and Plans

Warm-up

1 Look at the pictures. Complete the weather expressions.

1 It's ....
2 It's .... 
3 It's .... 
4 It's .... 
5 It's .... 
6 It's .... 
7 It's .... 
8 It's .... 
9 It's .... 

2 Look at the information in the chart. Match the cities to the correct weather description. Draw a line.

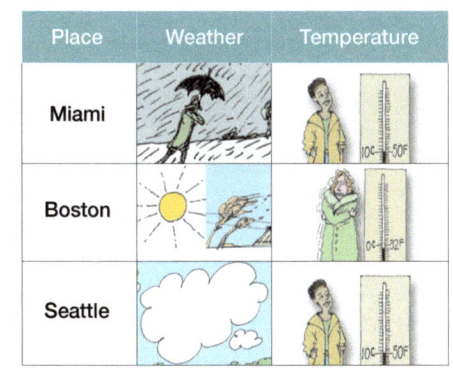

Place	Weather	Temperature
Miami		
Boston		
Seattle		

Place	Weather	Temperature
Detroit		
San Diego		
Chicago		

1 Boston
2 Chicago
3 Detroit
4 Miami
5 San Diego
6 Seattle

a It's usually sunny and hot here, but the weather is terrible today. It's raining and it's very cool.
b It's sunny, but it's very cold and the wind is terrible!
c It's a beautiful day! You don't need a jacket. It's sunny and hot.
d It isn't raining here. It's snowing and it's very cold. I need two sweaters!
e It isn't snowing, but it's windy, cold, and cloudy.
f It isn't raining, but it's cloudy and very cool. You need a jacket.

3 Look at the pictures. Circle the correct clothes.

1 a raincoat / a T-shirt / a coat
2 a scarf / boots / gloves 
3 boots / sunglasses / shorts 
4 sunglasses / a scarf / a T-shirt 
5 a coat / a T-shirt / shorts 
6 gloves / a hat / a scarf 

4 Read each sentence. Circle all the correct clothes for the weather.

1 It's so cold today. Oh my! It's snowing!
   a shorts
   b a coat
   c gloves
   d a scarf
   e a T-shirt

2 It's so sunny!
   a a hat
   b a scarf
   c boots
   d sunglasses
   e a T-shirt

3 The weather is awful! It's raining and windy.
   a boots
   b shorts
   c a T-shirt
   d sunglasses
   e a raincoat

4 I can't believe how hot it is today.
   a shorts
   b a hat
   c a T-shirt
   d a raincoat
   e a coat

DID YOU KNOW . . . ?
- The coldest temperature ever recorded was -89.2°C, at Vostok Station, Antarctica on July 21, 1983.
- Death Valley, California, US had the hottest temperature. It was 56.7°C on July 10, 1913.
- The strongest wind was 407 kph over Barrow Island, Australia on April 10, 1996.

LESSON 1

1 Complete each statement with the correct form of the word in parentheses. Use the present continuous. Use contractions.

1. She ......'s exercising...... . (exercise)
2. It's Sunday, so I'm .... a nap. (take)
3. Don't forget your coat and hat. It's .... (snow)
4. Today is Saturday. My children .... cartoons. (be / watch)
5. Lucas .... to music on his headphones. (be / listen)
6. .... wearing my sunglasses today. (I / be / not)
7. She's .... her teeth after breakfast. (brush)
8. Donna and Roy are doing chores. .... doing the dishes. (they / be)
9. I'm tired. I'm .... to bed early tonight. (go)

2 Complete each statement with the present continuous. Use the words in parentheses and the correct form of be. Use contractions.

1. (Tom / exercise, Marie / make)
   ......Tom's exercising...... and ......Marie's making...... dinner.
2. (they / bake)
   .... for tonight's party.
3. (I / watch, I / not / study)
   .... TV. .... right now.
4. (he / wear)
   It's raining, so .... a raincoat and boots.
5. (you / shave)
   .... before you go to work?
6. (she / put)
   It's cold this morning, so .... on her coat.
7. (we / start)
   .... a fire in the fireplace.

3 Complete the conversation with sentences from the box.

Bye.   Hello?   Hi, Valerie. This is Yvonne. Are you busy?   Oh, I'm sorry. Can I call you back later tonight?
Perfect! Talk to you later. Bye.   Well, actually, I'm making dinner right now.   Yes, of course. How's eight o'clock?

A: (1) ....
B: (2) ....
A: (3) ....
B: (4) ....
A: (5) ....
B: (6) ....
A: (7) ....

UNIT 9

4 Write Yes / No questions. Use the words in parentheses and the present continuous. Then answer the questions. Use contractions when possible.

1 (you / wear / sweater / right now)
   Are you wearing a sweater right now? — No, I'm not. I'm wearing a T-shirt.

2 (your / best friend / study / now)
   ....? ....

3 (it / snow / today)
   ....? ....

4 (your parents / watch TV / right now)
   ....? ....

5 (you / study / at home / now)
   ....? ....

LESSON 2

1 Write the time, date, month, or year.

1 right now: ....
2 today: ....
3 tomorrow: ....
4 the day after tomorrow: ....
5 this month: ....
6 this year: ....

2 Look at Marta's schedule. Match the events on the left with the present and future time expressions on the right. Draw a line.

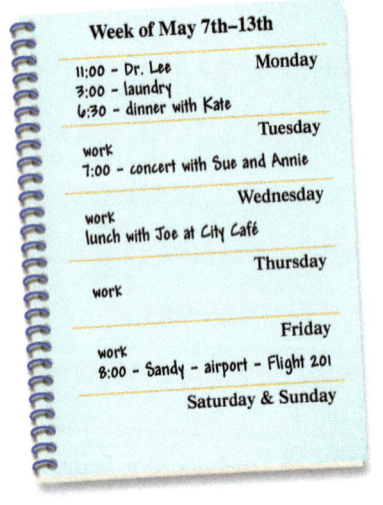

Week of May 7th–13th

Monday
11:00 – Dr. Lee
3:00 – laundry
6:30 – dinner with Kate

Tuesday
work
7:00 – concert with Sue and Annie

Wednesday
work
lunch with Joe at City Café

Thursday
work

Friday
work
8:00 – Sandy – airport – Flight 201

Saturday & Sunday

Week of May 14th–20th

Monday
work
dinner with Nancy

Tuesday
work

Wednesday
work
Jay's birthday party

Thursday

Friday

Saturday & Sunday

1 do the laundry
2 go to the concert with Sue
3 meet Sandy at the airport
4 have lunch with Joe
5 meet Kate for dinner
6 see Doctor Lee
7 go to Jay's birthday party
8 have dinner with Nancy after work

a the day after tomorrow
b this morning
c next Monday
d tomorrow evening
e next Wednesday
f this afternoon
g tonight
h Friday evening

78 UNIT 9

3 Right now, it's Sunday evening, June 30th. Look at Larry's date book for this week, July 1–7. Complete the sentences about his future plans. Use the present continuous.

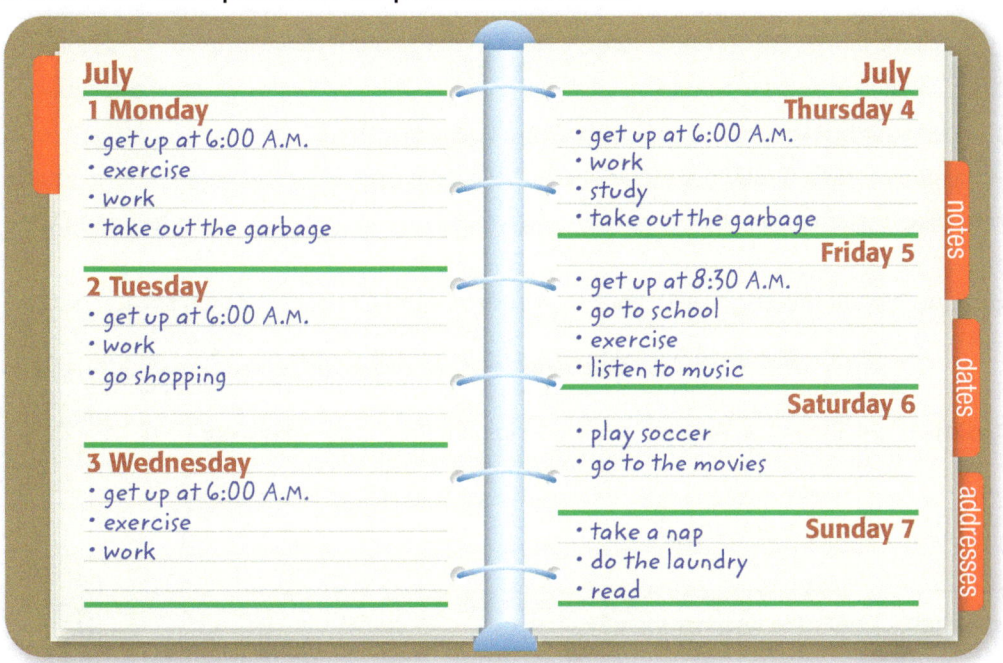

July
1 Monday
- get up at 6:00 A.M.
- exercise
- work
- take out the garbage

2 Tuesday
- get up at 6:00 A.M.
- work
- go shopping

3 Wednesday
- get up at 6:00 A.M.
- exercise
- work

July
Thursday 4
- get up at 6:00 A.M.
- work
- study
- take out the garbage

Friday 5
- get up at 8:30 A.M.
- go to school
- exercise
- listen to music

Saturday 6
- play soccer
- go to the movies

Sunday 7
- take a nap
- do the laundry
- read

1 Larry ....'s / is working........ four days this week.
2 Before work tomorrow, Larry ....
3 On Monday and Thursday after work, he ....
4 On Tuesday, Larry .... shopping after work.
5 On Thursday, he .... because he is going to school on Friday.
6 Larry .... to music sometime on Friday.
7 On Saturday, Larry and his friends .... soccer.

4 Answer the questions in your own way. Use the present continuous.

1 What are you doing today?
....

2 What are you doing tomorrow?
....

3 What are you doing this weekend?
....

5 Match the outdoor activity to the correct photo. Write the letter on the line.

1 .... go on a picnic
2 .... go for a drive
3 .... go to the beach
4 .... go hiking
5 .... go running
6 .... go bike riding

UNIT 9   79

6 Circle the correct outdoor activity to complete each sentence.

1 Bring your bathing suit—we're going (for a drive / bike riding / **to the beach**)!
2 This town is very scenic. Do you want to go (on a picnic / **for a drive** / running) to look around?
3 I packed a nice lunch so we can go (running / **on a picnic** / bike riding) this afternoon.
4 Do you have your backpack and your boots? Are you ready to go (**hiking** / running / for a drive)?
5 It feels so nice outside. Grab your tennis shoes. Let's go (bike riding / to the beach / **running**).
6 Your new bike is perfect. We should go (running / **bike riding** / hiking) with Ted and Diane this weekend.

7 Respond to the instant messages with your own information. Create your own screen name.

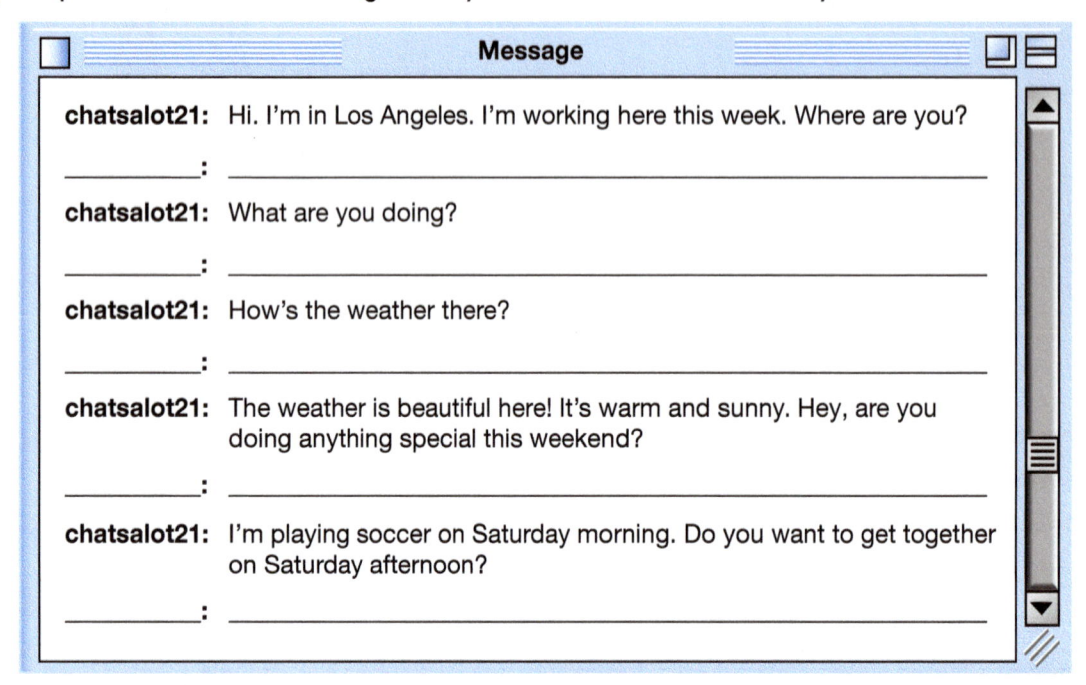

Message

chatsalot21: Hi. I'm in Los Angeles. I'm working here this week. Where are you?

_____: _____

chatsalot21: What are you doing?

_____: _____

chatsalot21: How's the weather there?

_____: _____

chatsalot21: The weather is beautiful here! It's warm and sunny. Hey, are you doing anything special this weekend?

_____: _____

chatsalot21: I'm playing soccer on Saturday morning. Do you want to get together on Saturday afternoon?

_____: _____

LESSON 3

1 Complete the conversations. Use the present continuous form of the words in parentheses or a question word.

1 **A:** What ......*is she studying*......? (she / study)
   B: English.
2 **A:** What .... to the conference? (you / wear)
   B: My blue suit.
3 **A:** Where .... hiking this weekend? (she / go)
   B: On a local wildflower trail.
4 **A:** .... are you texting?
   B: My daughter. She's supposed to meet me here.
5 **A:** What color hat .... ? (he / wear)
   B: A red one.
6 **A:** .... are you traveling this year?
   B: To the Grand Canyon.

2 Look at the picture. Then read the answers and write questions about the family's activities. Use **Who's**, **What's**, and **Where's** or **Where are** and the present continuous.

1 Who's watching TV / Who's eating an apple ? The son is.
2 .... ? An apple.
3 .... ? She's playing in the chair.
4 .... ? The grandfather is.
5 .... ? They're going to a concert.
6 .... ? The grandmother is.

3 Complete the conversation with words from the box.

| And what about you | got to run | I'm working at | in the neighborhood | Long time no see |
| Lynea! Great to see you | No kidding | shopping for a new car | Wow | |

A: Bart! **(1)** .... !

B: **(2)** .... ! What are you doing around here?

A: Oh, **(3)** .... the coffee shop now. On Pine Street.

B: **(4)** .... ! That's great! I go there all the time.

A: **(5)** .... ? What are you up to?

B: Actually, I'm living **(6)** .... just across the street. I'm out **(7)** .... today.

A: Really? **(8)** .... ! That's exciting. Well, **(9)** .... Great seeing you.

B: Same here!

4 Imagine a very nice day. Write answers to the questions. Use complete sentences.

1 Where are you? ....
2 Who's with you? ....
3 What are you doing? ....
4 How's the weather? ....
5 What are you wearing? ....

LESSON 4

1 Read the interview with Seiji Tanaka. Why is he visiting Australia? Circle all the correct answers.

a to visit zoos, beaches, and parks   b to visit friends in Noosa Shire   c to participate in a race

Triathlon Magazine:
Interview at the Noosa Triathlon

Every fall, more than 8,000 people race in the Noosa Triathlon in the beautiful city of Noosa Shire in Australia. In this event, participants swim 10 kilometers, bicycle 40 kilometers, and run 10 kilometers. It's a very difficult triathlon! This month, we interview Seiji Tanaka, an athlete in the event.

TM: It's sunny and warm in Noosa Shire today. I'm talking to Seiji Tanaka. He is participating in the triathlon this Sunday. You're wearing awesome sunglasses, Seiji.
ST: Thank you! It's usually cloudy at home.
TM: Really? Where are you from?
ST: I'm from Tokyo, Japan.
TM: I see! So, you're visiting Australia this week just for the triathlon?
ST: That's not the only reason. I'm also visiting the beautiful cities and beaches, and I'm going to zoos and parks. Australia has interesting animals and plants. For example, we don't have kangaroos in Japan.
TM: That's true. And how do you like the Australian weather?
ST: It's gorgeous! It's sunny and warm. It's windy here this week, but I like that, too.
TM: Great to hear! The Noosa Triathlon is a big challenge. How are you preparing for it?
ST: Well, I'm sleeping nine or ten hours every night.
TM: Wow! How many hours do you usually sleep in Tokyo?
ST: I usually only sleep six or seven hours.
TM: And what are your plans for the rest of the week? Are you training before the event?
ST: Let me see. Today's Wednesday, right?
TM: That's right.
ST: Tomorrow, I'm going bike riding all day. Then, on Friday, I'm swimming in the ocean with some friends.
TM: OK. And on Saturday?
ST: On Saturday, I'm going for a drive. I usually don't prepare the day before an event.
TM: I see. And after the event, when are you going home to Japan?
ST: Next month. First, I'm visiting relatives in Sydney.
TM: Sounds great! Thanks for talking to me today! And good luck!

2 Read the interview from Exercise 1 again. Then check T (true), F (false), or NI (no information) according to the article.

	T	F	NI
1 The Noosa Triathlon is very difficult.	☐	☐	☐
2 Seiji is from Sydney, Australia.	☐	☐	☐
3 Seiji thinks Australia has an interesting culture.	☐	☐	☐
4 He plans to visit the zoos, parks, cities, and beaches.	☐	☐	☐
5 Seiji sleeps six or seven hours every night in Tokyo.	☐	☐	☐
6 Seiji likes Australian food.	☐	☐	☐
7 Seiji is going bike riding on Wednesday.	☐	☐	☐
8 Seiji plans to visit relatives in Noosa before leaving.	☐	☐	☐

VOCABULARY EXPANDER

1 Look at the pictures. Write the weather on the line. Use the words from the box.

a hurricane   a snowstorm   a thunderstorm   a tornado

1 ....

2 ....

3 ....

4 ....

2 Complete the chart. Write the months and the weather in each season where you live.

Seasons	Months	Weather
Spring		
Summer		
Fall		
Winter		

GUIDED WRITING

Describe the weather today and the clothes you are wearing. Write five sentences.

The weather is gorgeous today! It's hot and sunny. I'm wearing sunglasses and . . .

UNIT 9

UNIT 10 Food and Drinks

Warm-up

1 Look at the pictures. Write the correct foods.

1 ....
2 ....
3 ....
4 ....   
5 ....
6 ....
7 ....   
8 ....
9 ....

2 Match the sentences on the left with the foods on the right. Draw a line.

1 They are yellow.
2 Their first letter is the same.
3 These are sometimes white and sometimes brown.
4 Its name and its color are the same.
5 They have the same last three letters.
6 Their first letter is a vowel.

a eggs
b orange
c apples, eggs, onions, oranges
d potato, peas, pepper
e tomato and potato
f bananas and lemons

84 UNIT 10

3 Look at the pictures. Write the correct drinks from the box.

coffee   juice   milk   soda   tea   water

1 ....

2 ....

3 ....

4 ....

5 ....

6 ....

4 Complete the chart. Check the boxes.

	apples	bananas	coffee	juice	oranges	peppers	potatoes	soda	tea	water
I like										
I don't like										
I have in my kitchen										
I need										
I eat / drink every day										
I sometimes eat / drink										
I never eat / drink										

DID YOU KNOW . . . ?
. . . there are more than 7,500 types of apples in the world. The most popular apple is the Red Delicious. It was introduced in the 1880s. It's bright red, crunchy, and a little sweet.

UNIT 10

LESSON 1

1 Look at the pictures. Use words from the box to complete the conversations. Two choices are not used.

| in the fridge | milk | onions | on the counter | on the shelf | soda |

1 **A:** Are there any eggs?
   B: Yes. They're .... next to the tomatoes.

2 **A:** Do we have any bananas?
   B: Yes. Look .... next to the oranges.

3 **A:** Are there any .... on the shelf in the pantry?
   B: No, there aren't.

4 **A:** Do we have any .... ?
   B: Yes. It's in the fridge. Look above the milk.

2 Read the words in the box. Do you keep these foods in the fridge? On the shelf? On the counter? Write four sentences.

| bread | butter | coffee | eggs | lemons | oil | potatoes | rice | tea |

> I keep soup, pasta, and sugar on the shelf.

3 Write the words in the correct order to make questions.

1 any / in / refrigerator / Are / eggs / there / the
   Are there any eggs in the refrigerator ?

2 we / Do / have / house / the / any / in / beans
   .... ?

3 meatloaf / onions / Are / this / in / there / any
   .... ?

4 Is / fridge / there / juice / any / the / in
   .... ?

5 counter / on / tomatoes / Are / the / there / any
   .... ?

6 potatoes / shelf / any / Are / the / on / there
   .... ?

86 UNIT 10

4 Complete the Yes / No questions. Use <u>any</u> and the words in parentheses. Then answer the questions about your own home. Use contractions when possible.

1 A: *Are there any potatoes on the shelf?* (there / potatoes / on the shelf)
B: (YOU) *Yes, there are.* .

2 A: ....? (you / have / egg)
B: (YOU) ....

3 A: ....? (there / bread / on the counter)
B: (YOU) ....

4 A: ....? (you / have / peppers / at home)
B: (YOU) ....

5 A: ....? (there / bananas / in the kitchen)
B: (YOU) ....

5 Complete the conversation with words from the box. Two choices are not used.

| any black beans | bread, cheese, and roast beef | Good idea | how about | I'm hungry |
| Let's make a | my favorite | roast beef sandwich | some bananas | Uh-oh |

A: **(1)** .... Let's make soup.
B: **(2)** .... Are there **(3)** .... on the shelf?
A: I don't know. I'll check. . . . **(4)** .... There aren't any.
B: Well, **(5)** .... a sandwich?
A: OK. We have **(6)** ....
B: Great! Let's make a **(7)** ....
A: Perfect. That's **(8)** ....!

LESSON 2

1 Match the food words and the pictures. Write the letter on the line.

.... 1 bread
.... 2 butter
.... 3 cheese
.... 4 chicken
.... 5 fish
.... 6 meat
.... 7 oil
.... 8 pasta
.... 9 pepper
.... 10 rice
.... 11 salt
.... 12 sugar

2 Complete the food or drink. Write <u>a</u> or <u>an</u> for count nouns. Write <u>X</u> for non-count nouns.

1 .... apple
2 .... lemon
3 .... pasta
4 .... bread
5 .... tea
6 .... onion
7 .... juice
8 .... banana
9 .... sugar
10 .... tomato
11 .... egg
12 .... meat
13 .... cheese
14 .... pepper
15 .... orange
16 .... chicken

3 Circle the correct word to complete each sentence.

1 I like (bread / breads) and butter for a snack.
2 Too much red meat (isn't / aren't) good for you.
3 We need three (banana / bananas) for the recipe.
4 Do you have any (salt / salts) and pepper?
5 Sue drinks two (soda / sodas) every day.
6 Martin loves to eat (fish / fishes) on Fridays.
7 I don't like (tomato / tomatoes) in my salad.

4 Write a true statement about each food. Use <u>I like</u> or <u>I don't like</u>. Make count nouns plural. Do not make non-count nouns plural.

1 banana
   I like bananas. or *I don't like bananas.*

2 tea
   ....

3 fish
   ....

4 orange
   ....

5 rice
   ....

6 egg
   ....

7 potato
   ....

5 Write five questions. Use words or phrases from each box.

| Are there any
Is there any
How many
How much | **+** | apples
butter
lemons
salt
cans of beans
water
chicken
tomatoes | **+** | do we have?
are there?
in the fridge?
do you want?
on the shelf?
in the kitchen?
is there?
on the counter? |

1 .... *Is there any salt on the shelf* .... ?
2 .... ?
3 .... ?
4 .... ?
5 .... ?
6 .... ?

6 Complete each conversation. Use the correct form of the words in parentheses.

1. **A:** *How much bread* do we have? (bread)
   B: One loaf.

2. **A:** .... do we have on the shelf? (coffee)
   B: There are three bags of coffee.

3. **A:** .... on the counter? (tomato)
   B: Yes, there are. I see two.

4. **A:** .... are in the fridge? (carton / juice)
   B: Two.

5. **A:** .... to go with our soup? (bread)
   B: No, I'm sorry, there isn't.

6. **A:** .... should we put in this recipe? (salt)
   B: I'm not sure. Maybe one teaspoon.

7 Look at the pictures. Write the correct container.

1. .... onions
2. .... pasta
3. .... juice
4. .... bread
5. .... soda

8 Complete the conversation with words from the box. One choice is not used.

| Here you go | I don't like soup | It looks delicious | Sure! Are you thirsty | Thank you | Would you like soup |

A: (1) .... ?

B: Yes, please. (2) ....

A: (3) ....

B: You're welcome. Oh, and please pass the bread.

A: (4) .... ? How about a bottle of water or soda?

B: Water, please.

A: (5) ....

UNIT 10

LESSON 3

1 Circle the correct form of the verb in each sentence.

1. We (has / have / are having) two sticks of butter in the fridge.
2. When (you usually have / do you usually have / are you usually having) breakfast?
3. Wanda is in the kitchen. She (make / makes / is making) pasta and meatballs.
4. There are a lot of vegetables in the fridge. We (need / don't need / aren't needing) any more.
5. We (make / making / makes) veggie omelets every other Saturday.
6. No, thank you. I (doesn't want / am not wanting / don't want) salt on my fries.
7. How often do you (eat / eats / are eating) out at a restaurant?

2 Complete the conversations. Use the simple present tense or the present continuous.

1. **A:** What .... (we / have) in the refrigerator?
   B: We have milk, cheese, orange juice, and eggs.
2. **A:** My .... (paint) his living room this weekend.
   B: How nice. What color?
3. **A:** What .... (you / watch) right now?
   B: My favorite TV game show.
4. **A:** .... (she / want) sugar in her tea?
   B: Yes, she does. She likes sweet tea.
5. **A:** .... (Paul / work) on Sundays?
   B: No, not usually. But this Sunday he has to go in to pick up some paperwork.
6. **A:** On Saturday we are .... (go) to a theme park.
   B: How fun!

3 Complete the conversation with phrases from the box.

> Actually, next Friday would be perfect   but I'm working late tonight   It's my specialty
> Macaroni and cheese? That sounds delicious   No worries
> That's great. See you then   Would you like to come over for dinner

A: Hey David. I'm making homemade macaroni and cheese tonight. **(1)** .... ?

B: **(2)** .... !

A: Thanks! **(3)** .... I often make it on Fridays.

B: Oh, wait. I'd love to come **(4)** .... I'm sorry. But thanks for the invitation.

A: **(5)** .... How about next Friday?

B: **(6)** .... ! What time?

A: 7:00?

B: **(7)** ....

LESSON 4

1 Look at each photo. Circle the correct word to describe the food.

1 (sweet / **salty** / spicy)

2 (sweet / salty / **spicy**)

3 (**sweet** / salty / spicy)

2 Read the restaurant reviews. Then read the descriptions. Circle the correct restaurant(s).

Town Sandwich $
Lisa K., Centerville
I just love a good sandwich, don't you? This sandwich shop is near my office, and it's my favorite. It's small, but the sandwiches are really big. And they're cheap. There are ten kinds of bread, and it's always fresh. I love the chicken sandwich with lettuce and tomato, with potato salad on the side and a cup of coffee. They have great coffee! But there's one problem. From 12:00 to 2:00, it's very crowded, and there are usually no tables available. So, go early! Town Sandwich opens at 11:00 A.M.

Like Reply

Breakfast 24/7 $$
Hayden D., Bridgeton
This restaurant never closes! Breakfast foods are available in the morning, afternoon, evening, and all night long. And why not? Breakfast is great all day! For lunch, I often have their large fruit salad with apple, orange, and banana, and I sometimes order a three-egg omelet with green pepper, onion, and cheese for dinner. It's not expensive, and it's delicious. So, try Breakfast 24/7! Do you need another reason? This week, they are giving new customers a free bottle of orange juice with their meal.

Like Reply

Only Vegetables $$$$
Marcia V., Northport
At this restaurant, there isn't any fish, chicken, or meat on the menu. Just like the name of the restaurant, it's only vegetables. The chef is from Paris, France. He's wonderful. He makes lots of great vegetable dishes. I love the tomato salad with red, yellow, orange, and green tomatoes and the spicy red pepper soup. My wife's favorite is the rice salad with apples and lemon juice, and my daughter always gets the pasta with pea sauce. You make your own juice at the juice bar. They have all kinds of vegetables and fruits, and you choose the ingredients. I love carrot, celery, and apple juice. My family usually eats meat, but we don't need it every night. Tonight, we're eating only vegetables at Only Vegetables!

Like Reply

1 There isn't any fish, chicken, or meat on the menu. (Town Sandwich / Breakfast 24/7 / **Only Vegetables**)

2 It's near the reviewer's office. (**Town Sandwich** / Breakfast 24/7 / Only Vegetables)

3 It is open at 4:00 A.M. (Town Sandwich / **Breakfast 24/7** / Only Vegetables)

4 It's very crowded from 12:00 to 2:00. (**Town Sandwich** / Breakfast 24/7 / Only Vegetables)

5 You can make your own juice at the juice bar. (Town Sandwich / Breakfast 24/7 / **Only Vegetables**)

6 The reviewer often has their large fruit salad. (Town Sandwich / **Breakfast 24/7** / Only Vegetables)

7 The reviewer likes this restaurant. (**Town Sandwich** / **Breakfast 24/7** / **Only Vegetables**)

VOCABULARY EXPANDER

1 Look at the pictures. Write the fruit or vegetable on the line.

1 .... 2 .... 3 .... 4 ....

5 .... 6 .... 7 .... 8 ....

2 How often do you eat fruits and vegetables? Which ones do you eat often? Which do you never eat? Write examples in the chart. Then use the information to write four sentences.

	Eat Often	Never Eat
Vegetables		
Fruits		

....
....
....
....

GUIDED WRITING

Describe the food at your favorite restaurant. Use the questions as a guide. Write five sentences.

My favorite restaurant is Karla's Café. I eat there three times a month. I often have seafood soup. It is spicy. It has fish and . . .

Questions
What's your favorite restaurant?
How often do you eat there?
What do you usually order?
How does it taste?
Is it cheap or expensive?

UNIT 10